Fieldcraft and Farmyard

Fieldcraft and Farmyard

Groundwork for Beginners

by

Valerie Porter

SWAN·HILL
PRESS

Copyright © Val Porter 1992

British Library Cataloguing in Publication Data
A catalogue record for this book
is available from the British Library.

ISBN 1 85310 164 8

First published in 1992 by Swan Hill Press
an imprint of Airlife Publishing Ltd.

Printed by Livesey Ltd., Shrewsbury

Swan Hill Press

An imprint of Airlife Publishing Ltd.
101 Longden Road, Shrewsbury, England.

Contents

Foreword

We have wandered too far from our roots. In the space of perhaps two centuries, most of us have forgotten several thousand years of ancestral knowledge about cultivating the land and raising livestock, the twin foundations of all food production in every part of the world. We no longer learn by watching parents or grandparents tending the crops and flocks, because they, too, are too many generations distant from these basic human activities to remember the techniques. We can only absorb knowledge from strangers, or from books, or plunge into unknown situations trusting to fortune and to instincts which we have almost lost. We learn by our disasters.

This book aims to give some very basic information for those who are new to the land and are inexperienced in fieldcraft and farmyard management. It will explain, simply, the techniques which are the starting point for anyone who seeks to make productive a piece of land, whether it is an enlarged back garden, a two-acre smallholding, a fifteen-acre green 'moat' buffering the homestead from surrounding properties, or a small farm. It seeks to answer questions that the new landlubber is almost too shy to ask, because they reveal an extent of ignorance which some do not like to admit, and it builds on such rudimentary guidance by giving advice which even those who consider themselves landwise might find of value. There is always more to learn, and that is part of the satisfaction of fieldcraft.

Most of what can be learned comes from the past. 'Agriculture,' said Richard Jefferies, 'is a profession in which a man may, above all others, be excused if he manifests a certain amount of irritability at the prospects of change . . . Setting aside those who have gone into agriculture as a science, and adapt everything to commercial principles — and they are as yet not very numerous — the great mass of farmers believe nearly the same now as they did two centuries ago . . . However much the aspect of politics may change, Nature remains unaltered.'

That was written more than a century ago. In the meantime, farming practices (and their scale) have altered radically, and are once again about to change quite dramatically. Since the Second World War the emphasis has been on maximum production and it has been nobly and wondrously achieved — but at what cost? At the expense of animal welfare, of wildlife and landscape, of the taste and safety of food, and above all of energy. By 1978, according to figures published by the Ministry of Agriculture in this country, 28 per cent of the primary energy consumed in UK agriculture went into fertilisers and 21 per cent into petroleum. That is to say, nearly half the massive agricultural energy input came from sources which for centuries had been animal-produced and animal-powered — manure and muscles. Tractors and self-powered machinery absorbed nearly half the petroleum energy used in agriculture at the time; fertilisers accounted for more than a quarter of the energy used in UK agriculture overall and for a specific cereal crop they represented more than half the total energy required to grow, harvest and dry the crop. Think of the energy that has gone into producing your breakfast slice of toast!

Clearly there was room for better housekeeping: too many people were using overpowered tractors for minor run-around jobs, pottering around the farm with small loads of feed or fertiliser, or simply using the tractor as a means of personal transport — which is like hitching up a huge team of horses or oxen instead of a pony just to get yourself from one place to another. The waste of energy was on a much wider scale: artificially heated intensive livestock units were poorly insulated so that a lot of the heat went to waste without being recycled (think of the warmth in a cowshed heated only by the bodies of ruminating cows!); straw was burned on the field, or was baled, handled and transported at the cost of more petroleum inputs, rather than the straw's energy being utilised on the farm as feed, manure or boiler fuel; manure, especially slurry, became a liability rather than a valuable and powerful source of energy as a fertiliser or as a producer of biogas for fuel. Not only was agricultural energy being squandered by the unnecessary and extravagant use of non-renewable energy resources but also the potential substantial energy reserves on the farm were being ignored.

Early in the 1970s I was involved in surveys into the potential for recycling waste materials and wasted energy sources but our efforts were largely ridiculed. Today, at last, more notice is being taken of the need to recycle, but on the farm the tractors get bigger and bigger and the message does not yet seem to have penetrated. Perhaps, indeed, the agricultural industry will become more aware of its profligate use of energy and will seriously consider both the long-term implications of the present situation and the possible alternatives for recycling energy on the farm, giving back to the farmers the independence they have always sought as part of their way of life. Today's farmer is woefully dependent upon the manufacturing giants, the companies that make inorganic fertilisers, assorted sprays, gleaming and increasingly powerful machinery (which is often a symbol of status rather than of good farming). The art of farming is being overwhelmed by the technology.

The postwar agricultural revolution was necessary and valuable, and the achievements of farmers faced with the awesome challenge of a hungry nation after the war have been magnificent. But, like so many revolutions, perhaps their eyes were fixed so firmly on their production goals that they, and above all those who advised and grant-aided them, failed to understand the dangers of the means. Rather suddenly those advisers have noticed that all is not well, and yet another revolution is now in its stride, slightly to the bewilderment of those of us who have thought and practised 'green' for most of our lives.

The smaller-scale farmer has the advantage in this counter-revolution in that the more traditional practices have always remained more appropriate on a smaller holding: they are more economical and easier to adapt. But the small farmer can also adapt, with a large helping of commonsense, some of the bang-up-to-date theories of modern commercial agriculture. It is the balancing of the old with the new that makes farming a craft and an art, as well as a science and a business if that is the need. Achieving that balance is what fieldcraft is all about.

I Fieldwork

Each holding, and indeed each patch of land within a holding, has its own special character, dictated by a combination of natural environmental factors and the historical and present human influence on the land. All these factors need to be taken into account in assessing a holding's potential, deciding what enterprises might be feasible and most appropriate to the land, and then how best the land and its produce might be managed.

The main natural factors determining the success of a holding are climate and terrain. *Climate* is affected by absolutes which must be accepted, such as latitude and altitude; and variables such as rainfall patterns and annual mean temperatures, the variations in which can be counteracted; and also much more local problems such as frost pockets, which can be quite easily overcome. The *terrain* might be flat or hilly, lowland or upland, and influential factors include type of soil, natural vegetation and so on; these have no doubt already been altered to some extent by the agricultural history of the land, including tree clearance, moorland grazing, downland ploughing, organic manuring, artificial drainage and, more recently, by the use of various chemicals.

The art of farming on any scale from a window box to a huge estate is to know every inch of your land intimately so that you can exploit it by enhancing its natural potential, rather than fighting a continual and exhausting battle to fit the land to inappropriate enterprises. That is to say: start with the land, not the enterprise, and be guided by the land so that you can work in harmony with it, ignoring those who define agriculture as a controversy with nature. Farming should be a partnership with the land rather than a conquest, with nature as an ally rather than an enemy.

Weather

'A good farmer,' states a venerable bulletin issued by the Ministry of Agriculture, Fisheries and Food, 'knows his own climate.' This booklet, *The Farmer's Weather*, is essential reading for anyone who works on the land, because all those who do are directly affected by the weather and need to be able to anticipate its probable course. For example, *spring growth* does not start until the mean daily temperature reaches 43F (6.1C), and by this definition the season so well named as 'spring' might start before Valentine's Day in the Scilly Isles but not until early April in the Welsh mountains and considerably later in north east Scotland. The length of the growing season, likewise, is much longer in the south west, but of course this and the start of spring can vary considerably from year to year, with or without the anticipated greenhouse effect.

Then there is the *depth of winter*, as opposed to its length, though both are important to livestock farmers trying to spin out conserved fodder while grazing is at a standstill or out of reach. The frequency of severe winters seems to vary: taken in quarter-century chunks since the beginning of the 18th century, there is the hint of a pattern of peaks as each century turns, but this could be misleading and is anyway irrelevant to the everyday business of farming. It would be a rash gambler who would bet on worse winters as we enter the next century.

Rainfall patterns are of more immediate importance. As a broad generalisation, Britain is wettest in the west and driest in the east, where the land lies lowest; hence the east grows deep-rooted crops while the west grows grass.

Then there is the *wind*. 'Every wind has its weather,' they say: north-westerlies bring broken skies, sunshine and blustery showers, with the seasonal frosts (because 'the north west wind and an honest man generally go to sleep together' — they both become quiet at dusk); the gentler west wind brings our best summer weather and mild winters, but also gales if there is a deep depression; the sou'westerly gave its name to a rainproof hat for good reason and brings a wet haymaking or harvest but also mild weather and an early spring. East winds tend to be the farmer's enemy: from the north east they bring snow, from due east or south east they bring bitter cold in winter or very high temperatures and thunderstorms in summer. North winds are always cold and showery, at any time of year, while southerlies are mild and vaguely damp.

If the wind changes direction anticlockwise, the weather is usually about to deteriorate, and conversely a clockwise change generally promises fine weather ahead. But look to *clouds* as well. 'Detached' clouds usually mean fine weather unless they begin to develop vertically into large shower-bringing cumulonimbus clouds which, if big enough, could bring hail or thunder too. Layer clouds tend to mean rain in some form but there are exceptions: for example, thinly laid or corrugated clouds such as strato-cumulus and altocumulus. The most typical rain-bearers are in smooth layers, white when high but grey when the base is low — the altostratus and nimbostratus clouds associated with warm fronts and responsible for rain-forecasting rings around the sun or moon and often preceded by fine, high cirrus or 'mare's tail' clouds moving in quickly from the north west. Watch out for a thin type of cloud with a serrated upper edge seen on the southern horizon: this usually means a thunder storm within 24–48 hours.

Frost or *fog* are usually preceded by a sky which clears around dusk, with a dropping wind: if the air is humid, expect a fog, but a frost in season if it is dry. Frost can be a considerable problem but it is possible to anticipate particularly frost-susceptible areas

within a holding and thus be able to take steps to avoid them or protect them. For example, as cold air is heavier than warm air, frost pockets can be formed by cold air flowing down a slope into a valley or hollow, or collecting behind an intervening hedge or embankment which prevents good air drainage. Frost-tender crops are therefore better planted on slopes rather than in valleys, and the removal of boundary fences and hedges sometimes greatly improves a frost-prone site. The other alternative (usually more expensive) is to protect the crop: orchard growers sometimes use small oil burners, smudge pots or warm-wind machines, with limited effect, for example, while many gardeners take the precaution of jacketing tender plants in straw or shielding them behind wattle and similar screens.

It is as well to bear a few facts in mind in planning frost protection systems. For example, at night it is warmer over bare soil than over grass, and it is warmer over moist compact soil than over loose dry soil, so the best ground condition to reduce the risk of local frost is moist, consolidated, weedfree soil — though the effects on taller plants such as orchard topfruit would be minimal. However, a freshly irrigated potato crop will stand frost better than a neighbouring one which has not been irrigated; autumn ploughed fields have the advantage over spring ploughed ones. In fact, the most efficient frost protection is the use of a continuous fine spray over the crop, very carefully controlled so that a mixture of ice and water is retained at a temperature of 32F (0C) on the plant surfaces, which is quite an art! But be careful about mulching which, although it is an excellent method of reducing moisture loss by evaporation and protects the soil from being pummelled by rain and reduces weed growth, can produce disastrous frost effects on susceptible crops very early in the season because the minimum night temperatures in the surface layer of air just above a straw mulch are often a great deal lower than those over bare soil.

There are many *folklore* weather warnings and some are indeed worth heeding. 'Shine before seven, rain before eleven,' is usually quite a good bet: very often a sunny start ends in rain by lunchtime and, conversely, a dull morning turns into a fine day — but check your barometer. If it has been rising steadily for quite a while, or remains high and steady, the shine before seven will probably be followed by a cheerful, sunny day; if the barometer's movements are jerky rather than steady, and not high, the weather is likely to be changeable so that a sunny early start is quite likely to deteriorate into showers by mid-morning. On a cloudy morning, some say that a prolificacy of spiders' webs festooning the tops of grass and cereal plants predicts a fine day, and the same is true if the ants have cleared out their holes and piled the dirt high.

The moon, naturally, is a potent symbol in folklore. There is a strong belief that the waning moon is not propitious for the farmer: some say that you should not ring your pigs when the moon is waning or all the rings will soon fall out, nor should you kill them on the wane or the meat will not 'plim' and will be less juicy. Hay should be made when the moon is waxing, and animals should be wormed in the waxing phase too because the worms are said to be more active then. More realistically, a pale, watery moon forecasts rain, a red moon wind, a clear moon frost, a white moon 'neither rain nor snow' and a halo around the moon definitely indicates rain — soon if the halo is close to the moon but later if it is more distant.

A 'blackthorn winter' is not so much a forecast as a recognition of the fact that the flowering time or 'hatch' of the blackthorn (which is the shrub that bears flowers on bare twigs and, later, sloes) tends to coincide with a cold period of north or east winds in March and April, especially in the Midlands, East Anglia and south east England. The period is also sometimes known as the Peewit Pinch: the lapwings are usually breeding then and the pinch of hunger in the cold spell encourages them to leave the open fields and make for better pickings on the coast.

There is often, though not invariably, a 'little summer' associated with the week of St Luke's Day (18 October) and also with that of St Martin's Day (11 November). Less reliable is the prediction that it will rain for the next forty days if St Swithin's Day (15 July) is wet. The few days before and including that date are often noticeably warm — one of a series of warm spells which seem to occur with reasonable frequency over the years, just as Buchan's cold spells (based on records over many years) recur quite regularly. Alexander Buchan, born in 1829 and the son of a Scottish weaver, was a well known meteorologist and his cold spells were the second week of February (very cold nights), the second week of April (cool, unpleasant, low pressure and probably damp), the second week of May (cold all over Europe, with unpredictable frosts), the tail end of June and first few days of July (wet and cool, but not as reliable a cold spell as the others) and the second week of August (cool and rainy in much of Europe, especially Switzerland).

There are some other patterns which do seem to be quite reliable in forecasting even if you don't use seaweed. If June and July are rainy and unsettled, there is an increasing risk that the harvest weather will be unfavourable (oh good St Swithin!) and if Candlemas (2 February) is cold and sunny with the wind from the east, don't expect an early spring. Finally, keep a sharp eye on April and May as a foretaste of the year ahead: quite often it seems that a wet warm spring means a cold summer and wet winter, a cold wet spring is followed by a cold wet summer and cold dry autumn and winter, a dry warm spring leads into a warm summer and warm wet winter, and a dry cold spring to a dry summer and cold dry winter. Or not.

As for 'Oak before ash, we're in for a splash; ash before oak, we're in for a soak,' bear in mind that some individual oak trees are *always* in leaf very early, way ahead of others nearby. Which oak and which ash do you take as your standards?

Water

From September, 1990, all farmers using water drawn from springs and boreholes on their own land can only do so if they have a licence from the National Rivers Authority and they are likely to be charged according to how much they extract. Water is no longer a resource which can be taken for granted and used freely, and it is increasingly important for those who have livestock or grow any kind of crop to consider the most efficient ways of finding, storing, using and recycling water. Some well loved streams and small rivers are already beginning to dry up, seasonally if not permanently, from excessive extractions and the massive agricultural land drainage of recent years, combined with major road-building, site construction, forestry schemes and other developments, is surely affecting water table levels. The situation is dangerously complicated by the increasing problems of pollution nationwide from industrial, agricultural and domestic sources. You can no longer take water for granted in terms of either availability or quality.

If you cannot (or do not wish to) rely on mains supplies for the holding's water, you need to exploit the holding's natural sources to best advantage. The local water authorities can offer excellent advice and in most cases you will anyway be obliged to consult them to ensure that your water use is legal. The following are the most common systems of supply and storage.

Springs and wells

A reliable spring is one of the most valuable assets you can have on any holding — as long as it really is a spring and not simply a land-drainage outlet which might carry pollutants such as field run-offs or silage and slurry pit effluents. Wells and boreholes rely on water table levels over quite a wide area and their levels can be affected by other well extractions locally; they can anyway only be productive where the substrata are water-bearing, and the water will need to be raised, either by hand or by some form of pump.

Main Watercourses

Rivers and streams can be tapped by creating ponds, on-stream or off-stream, if you are licensed to do so. Beware of upstream pollution or the possibility that an upstream user might at intervals alter the rate of flow.

Ponds in such situations are created by means of embankments to interrupt or divert the main flow or to retain a diverted flow. Always allow for the greatest conceivable flow when planning embankments and outlets such as weirs and sluices or you run the risk that either your embankments are washed away or you cause back-up flooding. Dam-building on anything other than a minor scale is not for amateurs and it is important to remember that it will affect other water users both upstream and downstream, sometimes for considerable distances. In fact, any extraction from or contribution to the natural water system, whether in the form of rivers and streams or simply the natural water table, has its effect in surrounding areas: we are all linked to unknown neighbours by the water, for good or ill — and more often the latter.

Ponds and reservoirs

On a 'waterproof' soil like heavy clay, it is easy enough to create a pond if the water table is high by simply scraping out a pit down into the water table level (which will vary seasonally) and also collecting surface run-off and the lateral seepage of groundwater, i.e. water held in saturated rock. You have little control over its levels but the clay's impermeability will hold most of what is collected, depending on the relationship between evaporation rates, outflows and extractions compared with inputs from whatever source. On permeable soils like sands and gravels, the pond might remain reasonably full if the water table is very high but in most cases it will need to be lined to prevent seepage, using puddled clay, concrete or artificial flexible materials such as PVC or butyl.

To puddle clay, work patiently by degrees and apply it in at least two thin layers rather than one thick one. Spread the first layer of clay over the site 7–10cm thick at the most; moisten it a little to make it workable, then tread it thoroughly with your boots or a tamper (or put a few sheep on it), keeping it moist while it is worked. When the first layer has been consolidated, add another and repeat the process, adding a third later if necessary. Eventually the consolidated clay should be at least 15cm thick and can then have its surface polished with the back of a spade.

Dewponds are shallow, circular, man-made reservoirs of drinking water for sheep and cattle up on the porous chalk downlands of the south. They are designed to catch and store rainwater and are often sited at cold-spots where the morning mists tend to gather. The ponds are lined with puddled clay, thickly blanketed with straw and with a surface protection of chalk and rubble against damage from hooved livestock. The secret to the success of a dewpond lies in its proportions: the rate of surface evaporation must not exceed the rate of water collection and these are affected by the surface area and depth of the pond and the size of its catchment area as well as its actual siting. A typical dewpond might be up to 2m deep and 18m across.

Land classification

Agricultural land has been classified into five grades, based on a combination of climate (rainfall, transpiration, temperature and exposure), relief (altitude, slope, surface irregularity) and soil (wetness, depth, texture, structure, stoniness, available water capacity). These factors affect the land's potential for the type, quantity and quality of grass and agricultural or horticultural crops which can be grown on it. Upland and hill regions (Grades 4 and 5) are subdivided according to vegetation, gradient, irregularity and wetness, and are coloured yellow and light brown on the Ordnance Survey's Land Classification maps. Half the agricultural land in England and Wales is Grade 3 land, coloured green, which grows mainly grass and cereals but can also produce a limited range of horticultural or arable root crops. Grade 2 land, light blue on the maps, puts only minor limitations on the range of crops which can be grown successfully; and Grade 1, the cream representing only about 3 per cent of agricultural land in England and Wales and coloured dark blue, is prime land with little or no limitation on producing high yields of most crops.

Soils

There are also maps which classify the country's soils, grouping them into 'soil series' according to the basic parent materials and profiles. These are more complex in their distribution, of course: even a small-holding might have several different soil types within its boundaries. The surveys for these Soil Series classifications also form the basis of Land Use Capability classifications, which combine soil types with factors such as wetness, gradient, erosion and climate and divide land into seven classes, the first four of which are broadly similar to the first four Land Classification grades.

The main factors which affect the creation of soil are the parent material (i.e. the type of rock which is weathered to form the basis of the soil) and the effects of rainfall, temperature, relief, biotics and time, each of which contributes to the weathering process.

Soil is a mixture of mineral particles, decomposing organic matter, air, water and living organisms. Its value in agriculture is determined partly by the chemical nature of the components, partly by the size of its particles, partly by the proportions of the different elements and partly by its 'profile' (the depth of the different horizontal layers in a sample, including the top 'plough' layer, the subsoil and the parent material and rock).

Particle size

Soil descriptions based on particle size of the mineral content give the familiar labels clay, silt and sand. The finest particles are *clay*: they have smooth surfaces and this factor, combined with their small size, makes clay soils plastic, sticky and difficult to work; they are chemically very active, they can hold a great deal of nutrients and also a great deal of water, and they have character-istic reactions to moisture and stress. Next in fineness of particles is *silt*, which tends to offer the worst characteristics of the opposite extremes of clay and sand.

The cohesive nature of clays puts them in a separate category to the non-cohesive soils broadly described as *sands*. These have the largest particles, forming well drained soils which are light to work but prone to drought and low in nutrient reserves. They are usually composed of primary minerals from the parent material, especially silicon derivatives such as quartz and feldspar, and the coarsest sands are *gravels*. Gravel (or shingle) has more than 70 per cent stones and has been water-sorted; very stony soils contain 35–70 per cent stones, stony soils 5–35 per cent stones (by volume).

Most soils are a mixture of these components: it is the relative proportions that give a soil its character in terms of drainage, stability and fertility. Other main components of different soils include organic matter and calcium carbonate, and the proportions of these substantially affect the nature of the soil. 'Mineral' or 'organo-mineral' soils, which have lower proportions of organic matter and less than 70 per cent stones (by volume), are classed as sandy, clayey or loamy depending on the proportions (by mass) of sand, silt and clay-sized particles in the organic fraction; loamy soils are intermediate between clays and sands, and calcareous soils are those with a marked proportion of calcium carbonate.

Organic matter

The organic content of soil is complex and ever-changing. It includes living animal and plant organisms as well as dead, with the latter in various stages of decomposition as it becomes humic. Organic matter (OM) has an important effect on soil structure and stability, and it also contains vital nutrients which are gradually released by micro-organisms and made available to plants. A good organic content makes soil generally easier to work and manage, though in some circumstances it is better *not* to cultivate, or at least reduce soil disruption, in order to gain greatest benefit from the soil's organic matter.

Very light soils have an OM content of perhaps 1–1.5 per cent; ordinary heavy soils 3–4 per cent; peaty soils 20–35 per cent, and actual peat anything from 35 per cent to 100 per cent. Undecayed OM can help to open up heavy soils. Well-decayed OM is *humus*, which improves the moisture retention of light soils and gives clays a better structure with the help of lime and worms. OM breaks down most rapidly in warm, moist soils which are well limed and well aerated, or most slowly in acid, waterlogged conditions. Typical agricultural methods of maintaining a good OM content are the use of farmyard manure (FYM) and composts, the ploughing in of straw and crop residues, and the establishment of leys.

Soil nutrients

The major soil nutrients, taken up by plants in relatively substantial amounts and with a role in building up a plant's structure, are nitrogen (N), phosphorus (P), potassium (K), magnesium (Mg), sulphur (S) and calcium (Ca). The calcium content affects the acidity or pH of the soil (see LIMING). Note that potassium has a special relationship with sodium (Na); indeed, several soil elements, major and minor, interact with each other in specific ways which can affect the health of plants and thus of the animals which graze them. This is especially the case with the host of micronutrients which are essential for plants in that they play important roles in the enzyme systems which affect function (rather than structure). They include copper, zinc, manganese, boron, molybdenum and iron in particular, also other trace elements essential to animals (such as iodine and selenium) and all sorts of 'heavy metals' like cadmium, chromium, lead, nickel and tin which can become contaminants, perhaps from the application of sewage sludge.

As plants, which absorb many of these soil elements during their growth, are the basis of the food chain and the means by which livestock obtain nutrients, clearly it is important that you should know as much as possible about the composition of your soil and monitor the changing proportions of its elements to ensure that there is a healthy balance between mineral deficiencies and excesses. Quite often the sickness of an animal can be traced to soil minerals — particularly familiar problems such as 'grass staggers' (a result of magnesium deficiency), copper deficiency symptoms such as anaemia and reduced growth rates, or manganese deficiencies leading to infertility in cows.

Soil sampling

The simplest ways of deciding what type of soil you are dealing with include checking a Soil Classification map, asking the locals, guessing from plant indicators, having a proper laboratory analysis, or using a garden-centre kit for acidity and doing the hand test for texture by rolling a ball of moistened soil in your hand to find out what it feels like.

In any field, the soil is variable and the art of good sampling is to try to obtain a representative picture of the field by taking samples from at least two dozen different sites, evenly distributed over the whole area. Start near a corner and follow a more or less W-shaped route but avoid headlands (existing or recently obliterated), waterlogged patches, markedly unthrifty pockets and areas near gateways. For permanent grass or long-term leys, take core samples to a depth of 75 cm; for arable crops, short-term leys or potential areas for re-seeding, use a core sampler or screw auger to a depth of 15 cm; for direct-drilled crops in stubble or grassland, take a separate sample of the top 2–3 cm as well to check for surface acidity.

Put the samples straight into *new* polythene bags. (Washed ones might contain misleading traces, and metal containers will contribute their own elements.) Laboratories can analyse the samples for pH and various nutrient levels but not for the amount of nitrogen likely to be available to growing plants; however, the latter can be estimated on the basis of previous cropping patterns taking into account the type of crop, the number of years since the area was ploughed out, the extent of crop residues and a history of the application of FYM or slurry.

You also need to know about the approximate proportions of sand, silt, clay and organic matter in the soil, because these textural qualities affect the soil's behaviour under cultivation and its ability to absorb moisture and chemicals. The organic content is usually very dark in colour and feels soft, silky and slightly sticky. For your own field check of the other components take a sample handful, moisten it lightly and rub some of it between your finger and thumb. Note whether it feels gritty, smooth or sticky, or with no dominant texture, and whether it stains your fingers. Test to see if it can easily be formed into a ball and then into a 'worm', and whether it can be polished. Many soils, of course, are combinations of the main components and there are many gradations of the main properties, but Appendix 1 takes you through the possibilities.

At its most basic level: sand feels gritty, clay feels sticky and silt feels silky. Loams are mixtures of these three, usually in fairly even proportions so that the texture does not fall obviously into a single category; they can quite easily be formed into a ball, with the particles binding well together, and the ball will take a slight polish. Sandy loams feel more gritty, while clay loams feel more sticky and take a good polish.

The characteristics and qualities of different soils are described in Appendix 2.

Soil improvement
Organic farming

To explain organic farming requires a whole book but the essence is to work with the land rather than against it. Your first step is to approach the Soil Association for advice and get hold of a copy of their *Standards for Organic Agriculture*. After years of being considered cranks, organic producers are now really coming into their own and being taken seriously by commercial farmers, who are rapidly changing their attitudes with the increasing evidence of a market demand for organic food. That includes not just organically grown vegetables but also 'organic meat', which is actually much more difficult to achieve because all the animal's food needs to be organically grown and that probably means growing all the cereals yourself rather than buying in concentrates, as well as making your own hay. It also entails a very high degree of animal husbandry so that you do not rely heavily on veterinary pharmaceuticals (and certainly not on growth promoters): the aim is for the animals to be so well cared for and under a minimum of stress that they are intrinsically more healthy anyway.

The initial stages of converting a conventional farm to organic standards usually involve putting down a substantial proportion of the land to grass and legume leys, and that means introducing livestock into what might have been previously an arable holding. For many farmers this means a radical change of attitude and management, including rather more labour for cultivations and for livestock care, a need to update themselves on livestock diseases and welfare (a lot has changed in the last few years) and a completely different attitude to soil fertility and the war against weeds and pests. A fundamental understanding of the soil and the life cycles it supports (all of them — not just the crops) is essential and can be quite an eye-opener for some. It is back to muck being the mother of money, and to a full bullock-yard and a full fold making a full granary. Above all, perhaps, it is back to the best dung for ground being the master's foot: that is to say, do it yourself, and get mud on your boots.

Incidentally, there is an intriguing book for organic growers on a small scale. Its title is *Common-sense Compost Making* and it is positively redolent with ideas for making the most of garden and farmyard waste. First published in 1946, it was later revised by the remarkable Lady Eve Balfour and is now obtainable through the Soil Association. It is a real treasure and rather nicely makes the point: 'After all, cow manure is just plants, composted by the cow. She is the best compost-making machine in the world.'

Drainage

'Draining is the art of removing superabundant moisture from the surface of the earth, and is often indispensable in the cultivation and improvement of the soil. The land may be cleaned and fallowed in the most judicious and perfect manner — it may be manured with the most costly dressings — yet, if it be not divested of that prejudicial excess of moisture, alike injurious to vegetation and the prospects of the farmer, it will generally be found a useless expenditure of capital and labour.'

[*The Library of Agricultural and Horticultural Knowledge,* published by J. Baxter of Lewes, 3rd edition, 1834]

If land is not free-draining the results can be frustrating problems with cultivation, bogged-down machinery, poaching by livestock, puddles, stagnation, parasites and mosquitoes, rush-type weeds, pallid crops and later growth in spring. Natural drainage is affected by soil structure, land contours and water table levels; artificial drainage can be by a combination of attention to soil structure and the installation of systems designed to carry away excess water more quickly. The latter, on a wide scale, is beginning to cause problems in that the very speed with which rainwater is conveyed by drainage systems into the rivers alters the whole balance of the natural water networks and can lead to lowland flooding of river basins.

Be that as it may, bad drainage is a local problem on the holding though the effects of draining the land in a wider context need to be remembered. Think on this quote from *The Field* magazine in 1919:

'It is sometimes thought that the necessity for keeping main-drainage channels clear is confined to the Fenlands or other low-lying areas, which are liable to inundation. In many places, winter flooding is regarded as a normal and inevitable condition of those lands, and indeed it is true that certain classes of grass land derive benefit from an occasional brief flooding, if it occurs in the proper season to provide a top dressing of river silt. But a sudden summer flood may carry away the hay or destroy valuable crops of potatoes or corn, causing heavy loss to the farmers who are affected by the catastrophe.

However, it is not only to prevent the disastrous effects of summer floods that the main-drainage is needed. Every agriculturist knows the benefits derived from field drainage in its various forms. To quote from an early writer: "While land remains in a wet state the manure laid upon it is, comparatively speaking, of little use; the seed sown often perishes; the crops are sickly and later of ripening; and the operations of harvest are attended with perhaps injury to the soil, uncertainty, and danger. The beneficial effects of draining on grass land are also very great. It is less liable to be poached, rushes and other aquatic plants soon disappear; the finer grasses rise in abundance, the pastures maintain a greater number of cattle and sheep, the stock becomes superior in quality and less subject to disease, and if the land be mown the hay produced is much improved in quality."

The defects . . . can be cured . . . by field drains that carry the subsoil water to the stream or main dyke, provided that these in their turn — and the rivers they feed — are capable of carrying off the water. But if they are not, what is the use of the field drains? Who will spend money on a drain that has no outlet?

In many parts of England there are fine systems of arterial drainage, formed by the practical sense of our forefathers, which have been neglected of late years till they are almost derelict. In other parts there are natural rivers; and it is no exaggeration to say that the majority of the English rivers are so clogged up by shoals, mudbanks, ingrowing trees, and similar obstructions, that they cannot discharge one of their main functions — that of carrying off surplus water from agricultural land. The cleansing and thorough restoration of these main-drainage channels, natural as well as artificial, is one of the first necessities for increased production in this country.'

Seventy years later, some people are complaining that the careless application of grant aid since the war has encouraged field draining where it was unnecessary (or undrainable) to the detriment of low-lying land in the river basins and sometimes of the fields themselves. Yet between 1840 and 1870 the farm labourers of England and Wales drained 200,000 acres of farmland a year, by hand — a rate not exceeded until the late 1970s, and then by means of expensive machinery. Even now, drainage contractors find very few fields which do not throw up evidence of the previous century's old clay-tile drains. Indeed, drainage on a massive scale has altered the face of the countryside at regular intervals and its consequences are probably still misunderstood.

Drainage tests

If a field is badly drained, you have work to do. Take out a sample spadeful and look at its colour. Permanently waterlogged subsoils tend to look blackish or bluey-grey rather than shades of red, brown, yellow and orange, and mottled colours suggest at least seasonal waterlogging. Dig out holes about half a metre square and half a metre deep, here and there, and pour a bucketful of water into each. If the water does not drain away within about half an hour, either an old field drainage system has failed, or there never was one. If you actually *want* to have a pond, dig test pits on the site in pairs and fill one of each with water, leaving the other to fill itself, then watch what happens over the next week or two. If the artificially filled pit drains quickly, your pond will need to be lined; the level of the water in the other pit suggests the natural level of the local water table.

Field drainage systems

The main systems of field drainage are by open ditch, by a network of underground pipes, by 'mole' drains (which involve mechanically excavating molerun-like channels underground) or by a combination of these systems.

Open ditches

At its simplest, an open ditch should catch water *before* it enters a sloped field and carry it away from the site, i.e. it should be dug out along the contours of the higher

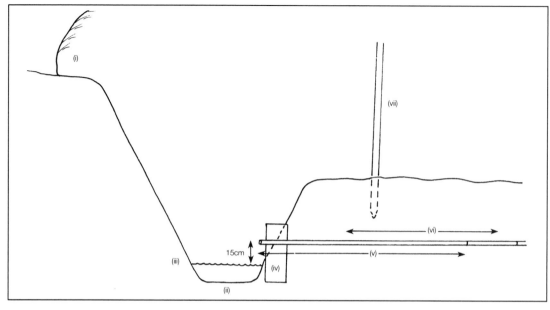

(a) Ditch with outfall from main land drain

(i) Hedge and bank	(v) 1.5–2m continuous outfall pipe issuing 15cm
(ii) Ditch	above normal water level
(iii) Normal water level in ditch	(vi) Main land drain
(iv) Headwall	(vii) Livestock fence (one strand of barbed-wire)

boundaries. Ditches are often merely channels to carry water away from an underground drainage system, or form a series of small open channels to drain hill grazing or lowlying meadowland.

With any system involving the flow of water, always take into account the maximum flow — for example in times of spate after heavy rainfall. A ditch should be deep enough so that its base is at least 25cm below any field drain outlets which empty into it, for a start, and its depth should also be adjusted according to the level of the local water table.

Its width depends on a combination of capacity to deal with anticipated flows and the type of soil in which it is dug. In general, make the width at the top equal to the sum of the depth plus the width at the base. A typical small field ditch would be about 45cm wide on its floor, 1.5m wide at the top and a metre deep. A well designed ditch is not too wide (or the water will create its own narrow channel and will deposit silt) nor are its sides so steep that they collapse. The

degree of slope of the sides must depend to some extent on the stability of the soil, with light soils needing a more shallow slope than heavy clays, and if you have any consideration for wildlife bear in mind that a steep bank makes a difficult exit for all sorts of animals and waterfowl.

The main problem with ditches is one of maintenance, and it ceases to be a problem if maintenance is carried out regularly by clearing the ditches out annually or biennially to their original depth. Take a look at the ditch after several hours of heavy rain to check its efficiency. Fence off ditches from inquisitive livestock, setting a strand or two of post-and-wire at least 45cm from the edges.

Land drains
Field or land drains involve a network of pipes, usually emptying into a ditch. Originally they were series of trenches in which open-jointed clay tile drains or inverted U-pipes were laid before the trenches were backfilled with gravel and the excavated topsoil to a

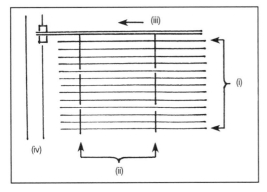

(b) Part of land drain system

  (i) Mole drains across laterals
  (ii) Laterals flowing to main drain
  (iii) Main drain flowing to ditch
  (iv) Ditch

depth of 12–15in. Long ago, during and after the Napoleonic wars, prisoners of war laid inverted V-section tiles; from 1750 to 1825 half-rounds and horseshoe shapes with flanges were used, and in 1845 the first extruded drains. Today the choice of materials is greater and, as well as clay tiles, includes porous concrete or plastic. The pipes are laid as a network of laterals (often in a herringbone pattern) running down to larger-diameter main drains. The pattern of the system and the diameters of the pipes depend on local rainfall averages, the size of the area to be drained, the fall of the land and the structure of the soil. The aim is to help the water to move away from the surface of the field and also to lower the underground water table, and there is quite an art in planning a good drainage system.

Plastic and polythene pipes might be smooth, rigid sections or continuous flexible corrugated lengths, with water inlet holes along them, and they are generally laid with the help of special machinery, usually by a contractor. Clay tiles are simply butted together (the water seeps through natural irregularities in the material), but special couplings are needed to join laterals to mains, whether of plastic or clay, and you also need outlet pipes at the ditch outfall. These outlets might need protection from accidental damage by livestock or vehicles and equipment used in ditch clearance. The

outfall should be at least 15cm above the normal water level of the ditch, and should be protected from inquisitive vermin by means of a grid.

Begin your excavations at the lowest point of the scheme so that ground water can drain away from your work right from the start. In low-lying areas, you'll need lots of ditches. On fine-textured soils such as clay or loam, the laterals need to be back-filled with gravel or clinker to give a pathway for the surface water's percolation down to the drains.

Mole drains

Mole drains are a cheap system for stone-free clay subsoils with a landfall of 5–10cm per chain and a reasonably smooth surface. They are made by a torpedo-shaped mole plough which carves a self-supporting cylindrical channel through the subsoil leaving

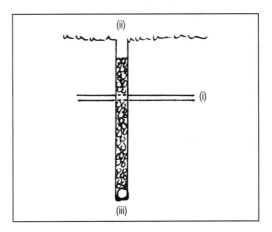

(c) Mole drains

  (i) Mole drain, channelled through
  (ii) permeable infill over
  (iii) lateral drain

no more than a slit above it. The timing must be right: the subsoil needs to be damp enough to be plastic and to retain the shape of the mole channel (no pipes are installed) but sufficiently dry to form cracks above the channel as the mole plough passes, because these will be the route for surface water to reach the channels. The top of the ground needs to be dry enough for tractor wheels to have a good grip, and the tractor speed should be slow. Moles can either be set in the furrows of a ridge-and-furrow field or up to 3–4m apart, following natural undulations and slopes where appropriate or, on flatter land, in a variety of patterns (fanning to one outlet, as a grid with mains on the boundaries, in an efficient herringbone or with the laterals following the ridge-and-furrow, for example). The gradients need not follow the landfall exactly: they can become deeper over the drain's length. The moles are set 50–75cm deep and are 7.5cm in diameter.

For best results, moles are ploughed at right angles over tiled or plastic drains, through their porous backfill so that the gravel connects moles and land drains. They are redrawn every 5–10 years. The drains should be at 2-chain centres (40m) with the moles at 2.7m centres (9ft), or at 3-chain (60m) and 2m respectively. The minimum depth of the drain at its highest point should equal the depth of moling plus a clearance of about 10cm.

Irrigation

In dry times, plants rely on the soil's ability to retain water, which depends on the soil's type, consolidation and OM content and on transpiration rates. Initially, plant growth depends on temperature: the warmer it is above 43F (6.1C), the quicker the growth — *if* the plants have access to moisture in the soil. Transpiration, or the conversion of water into vapour returned to the atmosphere and thus lost from the soil, needs energy from the sun to occur and, as it happens, the areas of Britain where rainfall is lowest are also where transpiration tends to be highest so that there can be an imbalance between rain input and transpiration output. During summer, when temperatures and extra day-length increase the plant's potential to grow, more and more moisture is removed from the soil by the plants and reserves are gradually used up so that soil moisture is in deficit. Usually the situation is rectified by the climate after September, when rain input has a chance to exceed transpiration output as the days shorten and the amount of solar energy decreases. By the end of

most years the deficit has been wiped out, reserves are replenished and the soil itself has absorbed water to the limit of its capacity so that the drainage systems begin to flow again and, if the rains are prolonged, flooding could follow.

Whereas artificial drainage is intended to remove surplus water, artificial irrigation seeks to overcome the summer deficit and thus keep plants growing regularly throughout the season at high levels, especially at crucial periods in growth cycles. Remember, plants cannot move around their environment to counteract stress, and it is therefore up to the grower to control the plant's immediate environment, including its micro-climate. Cereals are not too affected by lack of soil moisture, nor are deep-rooters like lucerne, but crops such as peas and beans and many others do benefit from irrigation even when sound steps have been taken to increase the soil's water-retaining capacity by, say, incorporating FYM to ensure a high OM content. Note that consolidated soil will hold more water per unit depth than loose soil.

The main choices of irrigation system range from expensive machinery such as rotary sprinklers and rain guns, to the simpler and age-old practice of damming ditches or making use of nearby watercourses. Deliberate flooding of riverside land from time to time is not so much to water it as to deposit alluvium: in the 19th century, 'irrigation' meant watered meadows and it was actually carried out in winter. A dam or weir was built across the river and fed by means of small, shallow trenches about 40ft apart and gradually tapering as they stretched away from the source at right angles. The trenches conveyed the water to the riverside meadow but as the aim was to maintain a constant *flow* of water there was a main drain at the meadow's lower part fed by several small drains which became wider as they reached the main. From the main drain, the water returned to the river or was conducted to other meadows to be flooded. Stops were placed at intervals in the feeder trenches (small pieces of plank resting on two little stakes, or simply sods) and were manipulated by the meadow superintendent in order to create an equal current over the whole area. The surface of the meadow was formed in low ridges, with the feeders on the tops and the drains in the hollows, so that the water was conveyed more quickly from feeder to drain. The whole business of 'floating' began in October, as soon as the aftermath had been grazed or a second hay crop taken, and the meadow remained flooded for a fortnight to three weeks at a time, the water never allowed to be still, then it was let off and the ground laid dry for five or six days before the cycle was repeated, with alternate flooding and drying right through to January, then flood periods were gradually shortened down to a few days at a time as the spring grasses began to grow. By mid March, stock could be entered in southern England's meadows, but not until May in the north.

Liming

There is an old saying: 'Lime, and lime without manure, will make both farm and farmer poor.' Another, from the 16th century, is: 'Ground enrich'd with chalk makes a rich father and a beggarly sonne.'

Acidity

The term pH is shorthand for 'potential hydrogen'. The pH value of any solution is a measure of the concentration of dissolved hydrogen in that solution and represents its acidity. Technically a pH reading is the reciprocal logarithm of hydrogen-ion activity but practically it indicates whether the solution is acidic or basic. (A base is a substance that reacts with an acid to form a salt and thus neutralises the acid.) The pH scale ranges from 0 to 14: 'neutral' water has a pH value of 7.0; acid water less than 7.0 and basic water more than 7.0. It is unusual to find natural water as acid as 3 or 4 and a reading of less than 4.5 would be considered very acid.

For the purposes of testing its acidity, soil is in effect a solution and is measured on a pH scale. An acid soil has a low pH reading; conversely, a higher reading indicates a degree of alkalinity. Alkalinity is more or less equivalent to the concentration of bicarbonate ions in a sample, as opposed to carbon dioxide: an excess of the latter results in acidity, but if there are more carbonates the sample will be alkaline, because carbonates and bicarbonates mix with acid and dilute it, whereas carbon dioxide dissolves in water to form carbonic acid. The most common factors in increasing alkalinity are calcium carbonate and calcium bicarbonate: calcium is the dominant ion in determining soil pH as well as being an essential plant nutrient.

Lime is calcium carbonate, and liming helps to redress soil acidity. The ideal pH for grassland is 6.0 and for many arable crops 6.5, so that liming is not needed if the soil's pH is already more than 6.5. Too high a pH, whether from overliming or occurring naturally, can lead to major trace-element deficiencies in plants, and thus in grazing animals. It can also alter the pH level in nearby watercourses: my mill pond's swan mussels greatly benefited from the run-off of a neigbour's newly limed fields!

A pH reading of less than 5.2 indicates a very acid soil, sometimes described as sour, a term which conveys a hint of some of the problems which soil acidity can cause to plants. Typical signs of acidity are patchy crop failure, lack of thriftiness, the commonness of certain weeds such as sheep's sorrel, spurrey, corn marigold and bents (grasses), and a mat of undecayed vegetation as a result of the acidity reducing the activities of earthworms and soil bacteria.

Appropriate liming rates counteract acidity, make nitrogen, phosphorus, potassium and calcium freely available to plants, affect the availability of other plant nutrients, encourage better root growth and greater bacterial activity to break down organic matter and generally improve the structure of clay soils. After the initial dressing (which in some cases might be quite high) calcium will gradually be lost again through leaching into field drainage systems, or because of chemical reactions with certain manures and fertilisers, or by removal through crop harvesting by machinery or by grazing animals which are then sold off-farm (note that lucerne, kale and sugarbeet are particularly heavy 're-movers') and it will therefore be necessary to top up by liming again, perhaps every four years, having had the soil analysed afresh.

You can check pH values yourself on a small scale with a soil-sampling kit, usually based on colour changes in the kit's medium. (Do you remember red and blue litmus paper in the school lab?) Garden centres sell small kits which might be adequate for a grower's purposes but it is important not to guess at liming rates. Have the soil properly analysed and heed the analyst's recommendations well.

Liming rates

Recommendations for liming applications are normally given in terms of the weight of calcium oxide which is required: the NV (or neutralising value) of a liming material is used as a comparison. It is expressed as the percentage of the effect that would be obtained if pure calcium oxide was used instead. For example, an NV of 50 per cent means that 100kg of the material would have the same neutralising effect as 50kg of pure calcium oxide. Thus a material which is cheaper in bulk is not necessarily more economic in terms of its neutralising effect, which is what counts.

For grassland, do not let the pH drop below 5.5 and use liming to bring it up to 6.0. For arable land, aim to keep the pH above the level required for the most sensitive crop; in general it is probably best to lime the land when the pH drops to 6.0, applying enough to raise it to 6.5. Tolerances of soil pH values by arable and horticultural crops range from about 4.5 to 6.5 and it is possible that crop growth will be inhibited if the values fall below these tolerances (see Appendix 3). For best results, the pH level should be well above the tolerances, which are minimums rather than preferences.

Liming materials

Soil acidity can be neutralised by applying liming materials such as calcium carbonate (in the form of ground limestone or chalk), calcium oxide (burnt lime, quicklime, shell lime), calcium hydroxide (hydrated or slaked lime), or magnesium carbonate combined with calcium carbonate (magnesium limestone) if a dressing of magnesium is necessary to prevent deficiency disorders such as grass staggers in grazing livestock or leaf yellowing in certain crops.

Calcium oxide is at its purest, then, in the form of burnt lime or quicklime but these can too easily scorch leaves. If water is added to burnt lime, it becomes hydrated or slaked lime (calcium hydroxide) and the chemical reaction or hydration can generate considerable heat. Hydrated lime, which has an NV of about 70 per cent, is expensive to buy but quick to act and apply. The most popular liming materials are basically calcium carbonate.

Claying

Marl is lime-rich clay which can be spread on sandy soils to improve texture and reduce the risk of wind erosion. The lumps will soon be broken down by winter frosts.

Organic manure

'Odes have been written and praises sung
To almost everything but dung;
But, oh!, what price is high enough
For such rich, aromatic stuff?
For no man spreadeth dung in vain;
He giveth to receive again.'

[Anon]

Once upon a time, what came out of the back end of livestock was valued for its fertilising and soil improvement qualities. Animals were either systematically 'folded' over chosen areas of land in order to manure it while they grazed, or their manured bedding was carefuly stored until it was in the right condition to be spread where it was most useful. Indeed, it was manure which sustained the agricultural explosion precipitated by the phenomenal increase in human populations in the towns and cities of 18th century Britain. The need to feed a landless population encouraged the rapid development of systems in which livestock were over-wintered rather than slaughtered for lack of winter fodder: the animal population was able to increase rapidly, and in turn produced much greater quantities of manure, which revitalised the land so that it was able to grow crops of far greater yield, some of which could be fed to the livestock, which proliferated so that more manure was produced . . . and so on.

Today, more often than not, manure is a nuisance because mixed farming is no longer common. It is bulky stuff, awkward to handle and expensive to transport from its point of production on livestock farms to its point of use on arable holdings. But, worse, because of the specialisation, the bedding straw that traditionally absorbed housed livestock's dung and urine and formed an integral component of farmyard manure (FYM), is produced elsewhere than where it is needed by livestock enterprises, and very often, therefore, disposal of the animals' effluent becomes a real problem. It becomes liquid slurry and potentially a highly noxious pollutant in that it is so rich in nutrients (including the nitrogen, phosphates and potassium so necessary to crop growth) that even a relatively small amount entering natural watercourses can indirectly murder fish and other life in the streams and rivers by depriving them of the water's limited supply of dissolved oxygen, which is commandeered by the bacteria involved in breaking down and recycling the nutrients. Some of the nutrients serve to feed rapidly multiplying algae, whose growth and spread deprive the lower waters of sunlight and oxygen and then, when the algae die in large volume, the decaying material creates a spur for even more oxygen-greedy bacteria. Run-off from silage, which is extremely high in nutrients, causes the same problem in the watercourse on an even greater scale because it is more concentrated.

If you have ever seen the dreaded 'silver sea' of dead fish in a stream polluted by silage effluent or slurry, or watched the creatures gasping for oxygen at the water's surface, you will appreciate just how essential it is that farmers, large and small, should be absolutely certain that such disasters are avoided. The problem is initially one of containment and then of safe disposal or,

preferably, disposal in such a way that the great potential value of the 'waste' is properly exploited on the land. Slurry and silage have the ability to generate plenty or, wrongly handled, to kill.

Manure

Farmyard manure is dung and urine combined with organic litter (usually straw) and deserves to be treasured even if it is bulky to handle. It adds humus as well as nutrients to the soil, unlike inorganic fertilisers. It varies considerably in quantity and quality according to the species, age and sex of the animals, their diet, the type of litter and its proportions to the dung and urine, and the way in which the manure has been stored. Appendix 4 gives some idea of the manurial values of FYM and of undiluted slurry (dung but no bedding material) from different kinds of livestock. The manure of fattening cattle, for example, tends to provide more nitrogen and phosphorus, elements which dairy cows and young animals utilise more efficiently from their food so that they excrete less of them.

There are two basic theories on mucking out: either change all the bedding frequently, or let it remain in place for most of the season, adding fresh bedding on top for a clean surface layer when needed. The former method makes for regular but reasonably light work, the latter for a major muck-out at the end of the season but with the two advantages that the accumulating manure can begin to rot down on the spot and, in the process, generates heat and also acts as an insulating mattress to the comfort of the livestock. It is said that a house cow will produce about 13 tonnes of dung and urine a year — half of it she can spread for you as she grazes, but the other half (at a rate of perhaps 22–27 kg a day) ends up in her winter bedding and has to be removed, carted, stored and eventually returned to the land. Do not be deterred by the work and do not stint the bedding — but bear in mind that if manure contains too much fresh, unrotted straw when it is spread on the land it could actually reduce the available nitrogen because the activities of soil bacteria in breaking down the straw could need more nitrogen than the manure contains.

Pitchforking manure is hard work. The first secret is not to dig in too deep: at the end of the winter, the bedding tends to become layered and you can almost peel it off laterally, rather than trying to chop into it vertically, so keep the angle of the fork fairly shallow. Then make full use of its long handle to ease the task: use your knee as a fulcrum on which to rest the handle once you have thrust the prongs into the bedding, then lever down with your right arm to detach a wadge and lift it a foot or two. This is much less tiring than using a short-handled fork. (Likewise with shovelling: rest its long handle on one knee, keeping your arms stiff and your body erect and straight, and you will be able to use minimum force from a slight thrust of body and knee.) Alternatively, of course, you can shift the stuff with a tractor-mounted manure fork.

Manure needs to be stored properly in order to preserve as much of its goodness as possible. The aim is to encourage it to heat in a heap so that it can ferment. Keep it moist, deny it air and keep it under cover so that the rain does not wash out all the goodness. Store it in a concrete-lined pit, to retain its liquid, and knock up a simple roof on uprights to protect it from the weather. Pack it down well in its heap.

For use in the garden, let the manure rot down until it is friable and sweet-smelling. For spreading on the fields, store it for at least two to three weeks before spreading FYM, partly to avoid any possible risk of contaminating grassland with *Salmonella* organisms from cattle or poultry manure, and do not let the pasture be grazed until rain has washed the manure from the grasses. Be wary of using any kind of pig manure or slurry in fields grazed by sheep: fattened pigs are often fed on diets with rather high levels of copper and zinc additives, and sheep in particular can suffer extensive liver damage on copper-contaminated pasture. Cattle manure, on the other hand, is high in potash and if spread in spring it could lead to hypomagnesaemia. Sheep will graze more readily than cattle after cattle slurry has

been applied. Poultry manure is high in nitrogen (watch those nettles grow!) and is best spread on pasture from March to September.

Dung used to be taken much more seriously in pre-NPK days. Early in the 19th century, for example, it was recommended that, if not spread immediately on the fields, the dunghill should be 'defended from the oxygen of the atmosphere' by a coat of sticky clay or marl and should anyway be 'defended from the sun' by being set under a shed or heaped on the north side of a wall. The dunghill's stone-paved floor should be gently inclined from sides to middle whence drains should collect any fluids into a small well from which it could be pumped out for use on the land because, as Baxter put it: 'It too often happens that a dense mucilaginous and extractive fluid is suffered to draw away from the dunghill so as to be entirely lost to the farm.' I shall not report the same book's recommendations about the Chinese method of mixing human 'night soil' with fat marl into dried cakes but would like to quote a tongue-in-cheek letter from a reader of *The Field*, written only a few years ago in response to another reader's request for information on the storage of manure:

'I must complain of the reply you offer as to the recommended manner of storing cow manure, your fault being mainly the failure to clarify the question. The most commonly recognised unit of cow manure is the pat, and it is not at all practicable to store pure pats, or small quantities of pats, in the manner suggested. These should be conserved as following and in alternative.

1. Sun dry the pat to a toffee-like con-sistency, then skewer with a broomstick and complete air drying by suspending from the garage rafters.

2. Scoop the pat with plastic bag not smaller than a copy of *The Field*, flatten, secure, and deepfreeze until required.

3. Dilute with rainwater and *mettez en bouteille au chateau*.

Any of these methods will preserve the pats far better than larking about with tented sheets, and furthermore, they will prohibit decomposition into a sweet-smelling friable mould which was not the object of the question. Method 3 is preferable in areas of low sunshine and intermittent electricity supply.'

Slurry

Slurry or liquid manure might be easier to handle than FYM but is not such a good physical conditioner of soil structure and its smell is less acceptable during spreading. Slurry is dung and urine without the beneficial absorbence of bedding; it is really only a problem with intensive livestock enterprises and so is beyond the scope of this book. Spreading should be judicious: as it dries, the slurry is quickly broken down by insects and bacteria so that its fertilising nutrients are made available to soil and plants but if it is spread too thickly it will depress desirable grasses and cereals in favour of weeds. Also, of course, the excess will probably wash off into local watercourses as a pollutant. Most stock will refuse to graze pasture for perhaps three weeks after it has been spread with cattle slurry and it is sensible not to let them on the land anyway until harmful bacteria have dried off — say a month after spreading or storage.

Other organic manures

There are many other types of manure from animal sources, all involving the once-again fashionable recycling of resources. Livestock carcases, for example, used to be buried under five or six times their own bulk of soil mixed with some lime and were left to decompose for a few months to 'impregnate the soil with soluble matters, so as to render it an excellent manure'. Indeed, old books recommend fish manure in the form of herrings scattered over the field (!), whale blubber, bones broken into half-inch pieces or powdered, horn shavings, hair, wool, feathers, blood, furrier's clippings, and tan-yard and glue-making waste. Bonemeal, dried blood and ground hoof-and-horn are still used today.

Manure is also a byproduct of vegetable matter, of course — for example, ploughed-in crop straw and other residues, green manuring (white mustard, fodder radish etc.), seaweed, shoddy (cotton waste) and so on. Old vegetable manures included furze tops (well trodden by cattle and mixed with straw to open the ground for Irish potatoes), rape cake for turnips (wireworms eat the powdered cake rather than the turnips!), malt dust, every type of seaweed (but said to be short-lived in effect) and kelp. Ten tonnes of seaweed would probably provide 50 kg N, 10 kg P_2O_5, 140 kg K_2O and 164 kg of salt.

Recently the Anglian Water Authority, in conjunction with Hensby Biotech, developed a technique for combining straw and human sewage into a sweet-smelling compost in three weeks. Mind you, the Chinese have appreciated the value of sewage for centuries.

Inorganic fertilisers

The three major components of inorganic fertilisers are commonly known by their elemental chemical symbols N, P and K (nitrogen, phosphorus and potassium). In fact, they are usually compounds rather than elements, typically salts of ammonia (NH_4), phosphorus pentoxide (P_2O_5) and potassium oxide (K_2O). The formulae for converting to the amount of the element from the two oxides are:

$P = P_2O_5 \times 0.43$ (i.e. 100 kg of P_2O_5 contains 43 kg P)

$K = K_2O \times 0.83$ (i.e. 100 kg of K_2O contains 83 kg K)

Nitrogen is used by plants in the form of minerals such as nitrate (NO_3), converted from ammonia (NH_4) by bacteria in the soil. As well as being 'in the bag', nitrogen is obtainable from the decomposition of organic matter (including FYM); it is also 'fixed' from the atmosphere by symbiotic bacteria on legume nodules, initially for use by the host plant but some will become available to nearby plants in due course, either through the soil as old legume roots die or indirectly through the dung and urine of animals which have grazed the legumes.

Nitrogen can be applied as a 'straight' fertiliser from various sources and in several forms (granules, prills, crystals, solutions or

25

as liquefied gas). Typical nitrogen fertilisers are ammonium nitrate, urea, sulphate of ammonia, sodium nitrate, calcium nitrate, anhydrous ammonia, aqueous ammonia, aqueous nitrogen solutions or gas liquor. Typical phosphorus fertilisers include ground rock phosphate, hyperphosphate, superphosphate, triple phosphate and basic slag, while potassium is applied as muriate of potash, sulphate of potash or kainit and potash salts. (Potash is the familiar name used to describe potassium when it is chemically combined in various compounds; the term is derived from the old technique of evaporating wood-ash lye in pots.)

Compound fertilisers combine two or more of the three major elements in the same bag. They cost more than straights and there is a wide choice of combinations. The proportions of each nutrient, expressed as percentages, are always given in the order N:P:K. For example, 20:10:10 means that the fertiliser contains 20 per cent N, 10 per cent P and 10 per cent K. Thus a 50 kg bag of 20:10:10 would supply 10 kg nitrogen, 5 kg phosphorus pentoxide and 5 kg potassium oxide. Fertilisers are usually offered in 50 kg polythene bags and are applied at rates of kg/ha, which is much simpler than the traditional imperial 'unit' rates (one unit was the equivalent of 1 per cent of 1 cwt, i.e. 1.12 lb or approximately 0.5 kg).

Depending on the form in which the fertiliser is presented, it can be applied to the field by various types of broadcasters or drills — see Machinery section. Note that fertilisers containing N should *not* be applied between September and February. With all fertilisers, considerable care needs to be taken to ensure that the timing and rates are appropriate and that excess substances are not washed into watercourses before they can be taken up by plants. It is essential to store fertilisers well away from watercourses of any kind in order to avoid pollution and it is also important that the store should be protected from any possibility of catching fire: watch out for combustible materials such as straw, hay, grain, fuel and oil and on no account allow naked flames or smoking in the store. If there *is* a fire, do not inhale fumes: call the fire brigade and in the meantime use plenty of water, but block all the drains first. Be extremely careful if you are welding machinery which has been used for fertilisers, especially if you are working in a confined space, because heating even small residues can be very dangerous and can release toxic fumes, especially from prilled or granular fertilisers. And when you handle these chemicals, wear gloves to protect your skin from possible irritation and wash yourself afterwards; avoid contact with or inhalation of fertiliser dust, too, as it can cause irritation in the nose, throat and eyes. Wash your eyes immediately if they become affected.

If the need for all these precautions alarms you — good! Try FYM instead. And just wait until you see what you are supposed to wear when applying sprays!

Cultivations

The main reasons for cultivating land before establishing a crop are to control weeds, to bury field trash, to hide seeds from predators and to alter the soil structure in order to provide an amenable environment for the germinating seed and growing plant. Traditionalists, whether in the kitchen garden or in the field, expend considerable energy in disturbing the plot by digging and ploughing but there is the other extreme of leaving it undisturbed and using mulches (organic or inert) to control weeds, or spraying if that is your style. Direct drilling is a mechanical technique requiring minimum soil disturbance: there is no ploughing and only light use of cultivators to create a tilth just deep enough for the seeds. It has the advantage of saving time, retaining moisture, building up surface OM and often giving better yields from cereal crops but it can lead to serious slug problems and persistent perennial weeds.

The main stages of mechanical field cultivation include ploughing (to disturb the soil and bury trash), seedbed creation (harrows, cultivators, rollers and so on) and seeding. The field might also be passed over for fertilising, weed and pest control and perhaps irrigation, and finally of course there is harvesting. Equipment for these operations is described in the Machinery section.

A tilth for the very small seeds of root crops and grasses needs to be as fine as possible with a level, moist, firm bed, and it is best to sow root crops on ridges in areas of high rainfall; for spring cereals the tilth should be reasonably fine but for autumn-sown cereals the surface can be left fairly rough after sowing, with clods almost as big as your fist to give some wind protection during the winter — they can be broken up after the frosts by harrowing and rolling. Rolling in order to settle frost-lifted plants and soil in the spring is usually good practice on cereal crops and grass unless the field is very wet.

It is important to stop and think before cultivations begin. Why are you doing it? Is it necessary, and are your methods appropriate? Is it possible that your operations are doing more harm than good, if not to your crops or grass, then to the environment in general? In 1900 J. Charles King wrote:

'The scientific farmer's aim is to grow good land, for land is grown the same as crops are. It is done by judicious cultivation and ploughings, to create loam by root growth, decay, and in-ploughings of crops sown for that purpose. The old name for this grown land was "humus".'

King was in fact discussing *ridge-and-furrow* ploughing, a traditional practice on wet, heavy land which was intended to keep it dry in wet seasons. Even with no fall from the furrows towards the ditches, the land above the furrow would dry quickly. There was usually a deeper 'water furrow' intersecting the land furrows obliquely, kept clear so that the water could flow to a lower level. The high ridges were created by turning the furrow to the ridge twice or even three times.

Ploughing

The point of ploughing is to break up the ground and at the same time to invert the top soil, burying trash and weeds — a practice not universally recognised as useful.

Each 'body' of a plough turns one furrow and there is plenty of choice of individual furrow width, the number of furrows which can be turned simultaneously and the shape of the body for different purposes. The coulter cuts the ground, the share undercuts the furrow slice and the mouldboard lifts and turns the slice.

The ploughing depth should not exceed two-thirds of the width of the slice. However, if ploughing is to the same depth year after year a 'pan' will be formed in the soil or subsoil. Soil compaction also occurs if the soil is too wet at the time of working: tractor wheels in the furrows smear and compact them, and the slice itself is smeared by the mouldboard so that clods are formed.

If you are using a conventional plough (which will have only righthand mouldboards), begin by marking a shallow furrow all the way round the field a few metres in from the hedge. Then use shallow furrows to section off the field into 'lands' about 30m wide, and form a ridge at the centre of each land. Now work each land separately, up and down on each side of its ridge to 'gather' the soil, turning the tractor to the right on the headland with each pass. Alternatively, use the time-saving reversible plough, which has lefthand mouldboards as well as righthand ones so that you can simply work across the whole field, from side to side, ploughing parallel to the longer boundaries in order to reduce the number of turns at the headlands. The drawback is that the reversible plough weighs a lot more, needs a great deal more energy to pull it and, naturally, costs considerably more than a conventional plough. It also has more parts to go wrong.

Cultivators

Some people do not plough at all but use cultivators to break up the top layer of soil without burying trash and weeds, or to break down soil clods on ploughed land. In essence, they are sets of tines which rotate, vibrate or rake through the soil. Harrows generally have numerous smaller tines on a simple frame and are used to produce a good seedbed or to comb through matted grassland. There are also many types of small cultivators which do not need tractor power but have their own small engines and are pedestrian controlled; they are widely used in market gardening, parks and large kitchen gardens and could be ideal for a smallholding. They are described in the Machinery section as two-wheeled tractors.

Seed-sowing

You can, of course, sow your seed by hand over limited areas and, from my experience, handsowing a couple of acres of grass on a warm spring day is a very pleasant pastime. It also gives you an inch-by-inch view of your land. All you need is a seed pouch, which is easily devised, some marking canes, a steady walk and a sense of rhythm. Broadcasting by hand is described in the Grassland section.

Machine seeding might be by broadcasting or by drilling. Grain drills are adaptable to anything from grass seed to beans, and deposit them in a steady trickle in rows; precision drills are for spaced planting, and direct drills have coulters which open up the ground and deliver the seeds into grooves. Grass seed is sometimes injected with slit-seeders into existing swards for renovation.

It is increasingly the practice to leave carefully spaced rows deliberately unseeded, providing *tramlines* for the wheels when spraying or fertilising after the crop has emerged, so that the growing crop is not damaged during the work.

The sowing of seed is an action ripe with promise and has of course attracted many a superstition over the centuries. Some of the folklore could be quite sensibly based, however it has been dressed up, but some is fairly ridiculous (like: always plant your potatoes at Easter — a festival which might occur any time from early March to late April). The moon has always been considered a potent factor in plant growth, and planting by the moon has a long tradition, according to which all crops which mature their produce below ground, such as potatoes, should be planted when the moon is waning, preferably in its third quarter, while crops which mature above ground should be planted when it is waxing, preferably in its first quarter. However, the *seeds* of such plants should be sown two days before the full moon, or with the moon, Mercury and Venus in the ascendant.

Weed control

In order to control weeds without resorting to sprays, aim to cultivate them to death and also look to a healthy, rapid crop which can outgrow and smother the weeds.

Annual weeds can be controlled by cultivating so that the weed seeds are encouraged to germinate and they can then be harrowed, hoed out or ploughed in as green manure a while before the desired crop is sown.

Perennial weeds are more difficult to vanquish except by the age-old practice of fallowing, i.e. cultivating the area frequently throughout the season rather than growing a crop on it, so that the soil dries out. It is possible to exhaust weeds like bindweed, dock, thistle and coltsfoot by constantly cutting off the top growth with a hoe (or perhaps using appropriate livestock to graze them off — geese for ground elder and sheep for docks, they say) but it will be a long job. An alternative is to carry a dockspade or thistle-stick with you whenever you walk the land, and do so often enough to attack individual weeds on sight, catching them before they set seed. Wild oats are still hand-rogued on some cereal farms — literally pulled out by hand once they are showing above the crop — but the seeds can remain dormant in the soil for a long time. Wild oats can become a serious pest, as is black grass on heavy soils, and both tend to be attacked with sprays or, until recently, by straw-burning to destroy seeds lying on the soil surface. Couchgrass can eventually be destroyed if you can drag its rhizomes to the surface (cultivate, harrow, rotavate) and leave them there to be killed by dessicating winds.

Bracken and brambles can often be controlled by freerange pigs in appropriate situations: the animals can really clean up the ground and leave it thoroughly cultivated and manured. Otherwise bracken needs to be chopped off twice a year when the leaves are almost fully opened and rotavated to chop up the rhizomes, or deep-ploughed, and then the area should be put down to a cleaning crop of potatoes or kale before it is eventually reseeded for grass. Bracken can be poisonous to livestock if eaten when green but it contains a fair amount of potash and makes a useful fertiliser in FYM if used as bedding.

In grassland, weed problems are worsened by poor fertility (weeds often thrive where desirable grasses and crop plants struggle), bad drainage, lack of lime, poaching by livestock, or overharvesting either by continuous cutting for hay or because of overgrazing. All over the country there are, typically, paddocks for ponies and horses where the grass has been reduced to stumps by constant overstocking and the thistles and ragwort run rampant. Ragwort is poisonous to most livestock and should be eradicated on sight. There is a table of other poisonous plants in Appendix 7.

Weed control is often simply a matter of sound husbandry. Tussock grass, rushes and horsetail, for example, indicate poor drainage and the infestation will disappear when the drainage is improved. The thistle forest can be deterred if overgrazing is avoided. Sorrel can be controlled by liming. Indeed, weeds are a good indication of soil condition. Ragwort actually suggests a loam good enough for any crop; a crowd of thistles indicates good rich soil in need of draining and cleaning; infestations of common dock and mugwort show that a good soil is incorrectly cultivated; corn sowthistle likes heavy clays, while sorrel, dead nettle, wild kale and corn marigold like light soils. Corn spurry likes rather a moist bed; nettles almost invariably indicate human settlement, past or present; wild mustard grows where there is plenty of manure; chickweed suggests the soil has been improved and would crop well if cleaned; marsh marigold and wild watercress in abundance suggest a river meadow has been overwatered; thriving white clover and daisy in pasture hint at adequate natural or artificial manuring by lime or marl, while natural red clover indicates a calcareous soil; yarrow or milfoil abounds in pastures on deep soils and meadow foxtail on soils which are deep and moist; common rattle abounds on exhausted or poor meadow soils which need manuring, and pry (the sedge Carex dioica) suggests there is stagnant water beneath a meadow which needs to be drained; couch grass abounds on land much cultivated and long cropped.

On the other hand, you could consider weeds more positively, not as weeds but as part of a well balanced ecology in which you admit there is more to the countryside than agriculture and kitchen gardens, or as potential crops. For heaven's sake, if they are so determined to grow, find a use for them! Even ground elder can be an asset: it can be cooked and eaten, or made into a poultice to soothe rheumatism and gout — which is why the Romans introduced it to Britain in the first place, they say. Even the Ministry of Agriculture has now realised that some of our native weeds contain large amounts of natural oils which could be of value in industrial processes and are seriously talking about the development of farmed crops of meadowfoam, alexanders, hogweed and cow parsley. Richard Jefferies, in *Meadow Thoughts* published in 1884, put it thus:

'The extravagance is sublime . . . Seeds by the hundred million float with absolute indifference on the air. The oak has a hundred thousand more leaves than necessary, and never hides a single acorn. Such noble, broadcast, open-armed waste is delicious to behold . . . Nature flings treasures abroad . . . Prodigality and superfluity are stamped on everything she does . . . The surface of the earth offers to us far more than we can consume . . . If I could but give away as freely as the earth does! From the littleness, and meanness, and niggardliness forced upon us by circumstances, what a relief to turn aside to the exceeding plenty of Nature!'

Other pests

As with weeds, the control of pests and diseases can be achieved by very good husbandry without having to resort to chemicals. Rotation is its essence: remove the continuity of the host plant or animal and you break the pest cycle. That entails growing different families of crops in different years, or grazing different species or ages of livestock over a field during the year. Learn all you can about the pest's way of life and then act to disrupt it. For example, craneflies lay their eggs (future leatherjackets) on grassland or weedy stubble in the autumn, so plough it before August. Sow brassicas too late or too early (any time except April and May) for the flea-beetle adults to attack seed leaves. Spindle looks very pretty in the hedgerow but it is a winter host for the bean aphid's eggs, and cereal aphids overwinter on grasses and woody stems as well as cereals.

Cultivations also help by exposing invertebrate pests to predators and by removing the weeds which are so often alternative host plants. Offering crop plants the best possible growing conditions (good seed beds, good seed, adequate nutrients and water for example) encourages a healthy crop able to grow away from attack by pests. If an area is known to be plagued by certain pests, admit defeat and do not plant what they will attack — crops like maize on chalk soils heavily infested with eelworm, or red clover in a field infested with fruit fly.

Another idea, now being more actively researched, is the introduction of specific predators or parasites to control pests and even specific fungal pathogens to control grassland weeds, but think carefully about possible ramifications if the predator gets out of control. Ladybirds, lacewings, hover-flies, hedgehogs and toads are all natural friends to the gardener and smallholder and even some of the giant plant protection chemical manufacturers are seriously rearing ladybirds on a huge scale as an alternative to crop-spraying.

Or use plant varieties which have a genetic resistance to or tolerance of various diseases, or mix up crops to 'confuse' the pest — on a small scale practise companion planting. Certain strong-smelling plants such as marigolds, onions and lavender might ward off certain insect pests and could even make one of two rabbits think twice, though my rabbits have never been deterred by anything except electric fencing or well-buried rabbit netting, and the local deer have never been fooled by the trick of decorating the boundaries with bags of human hair (no, I have not yet tried lion's dung) but they do respect the unexpected almost invisible stretched lines of plain green garden wire, flagged at intervals to prevent them garrotting themselves.

And then there are rats. Apart from keeping a place clean and blocking all possible entry routes to food stores and making sure hen houses have sound floors, protected by small-mesh wire netting, here are a few old remedies for getting rid of rats (not necessarily recommended in practice — they are rather unpleasant!):

(a) Cut a sponge into small pieces, fry them and dip them in honey: the rats eat the sponge, take a drink of water and so distend their stomachs that they die.

(b) Cut some corks in thin slices (as thin as a penny), roast or stew them in grease: the rats will die of indigestion.

(c) Mix one part of powdered ratsbane (nux vomica) with three of meal, flour or anything else a rat fancies: this will apparently kill without pain any animal which is of a species born blind (keep the dog away!) and so suddenly, in mid-meal, that they will die happy.

In 1813 fieldmice had become a plague in the Forest of Dean in spite of trapping, poisoning and the employment of dogs and cats. They ate not only newly planted acorns but even ate through the stems of trees seven or eight feet high and an inch and a half in diameter. The following method was tried, no doubt in some desperation. Specially designed holes were dug at twenty-yard intervals in an area of 3,200 acres and quickly caught 30,000 mice, keeping the Forest clear for two or three years. Each hole, which caught perhaps fifteen mice a night, was 18–24in long, 16–18in deep, with very smooth sides so that the mice could not run up them, and carefully tapered to be the width of a spade at the top, 14–15in wide at the bottom, and 3–4in wider every way at the bottom than at the top. Rather more simply, garden mice can be trapped in a large inverted flowerpot, buried in the soil with its base level with the surface and baited with corn so that the mice enter the drainage hole, have a good feast and can't find their way out again. (Note that mice can get into some difficulties with hexagonal mesh in this respect: they might wriggle their way in, as the stuff has a certain give to it, and then eat so much that they are too fat to wriggle out again . . .)

Moles might be considered pests in the garden but in fact they have often been considered as the farmer's friend, the 'blessed and innocent little pioneers' who annually give pastures their first top-dressing — and indeed at one time Scottish smallholders pleaded with their lairds to spare the moles, whose destruction by mole-catchers had resulted in the spread of livestock maladies such as foot-rot and 'the pining' previously unknown in the locality. You could try persuading moles to go elsewhere by putting green slices of leek, onion or garlic in their runs.

Crops

The type of crop which can be grown sensibly is largely dictated by the local climate. In Britain the wetter western regions grow excellent grass while the drier eastern plains, where harvesting is easier, are devoted to arable crops. Within that generalisation, the mildness of south west England in particular encourages the raising of early potatoes, flowers and other specialist crops, and the chalk and limestone regions of southern England provide sheep grazing, dairy cattle leys, large-scale cereal enterprises (especially barley) and the production of herbage seed. In contrast, other hill farms are devoted to rough grazing for cattle and sheep, and at higher altitudes the land tends to be afforested. Of course there are many 'in-between' areas but, in general, the heavier the soil and the higher the annual rainfall, the more likely it is that grass will be a farm's most dominant crop. Many lowland holdings are still mixed farms, combining crop-growing with the rearing of livestock, even in this specialist age, and with the new emphasis on diversification the return to

mixed farming could well increase. Certainly many smallholdings practise mixed farming in order to be more self-sufficient.

It must be remembered that the harvesting of crops removes considerable resources from the field, especially where they are sold off-farm. In an ideal environment, energy sources are constantly recycled: a grazing animal eats grass and homegrown winter food and returns at least part of the consumed nutrients to the land in the form of manure. As long as the animal remains on the farm, it acts as a store of some of the resources it has utilised but as soon as the animal or its produce (e.g. milk or offspring) leave the farm, those resources are lost to the holding. On an arable farm, a high proportion of the land's resources are removed from the field at harvest and must be constantly replaced if the land is to remain fertile.

Types of crop

The major types of crop (apart from grassland, which is considered separately) are cereals, roots and tubers, pulses, and forage crops or restoratives. Appendix 5 gives more details of likely field crops and their uses.

Cereals include wheat, barley, oats, rye, triticale (a wheat-rye cross) and maize. They can be grown in nearly all types of soil but the limiting factors are the ability to cultivate that soil in the appropriate season and to harvest the crop. For example, heavy clay can grow good wheat but, as every Wealden gardener knows, the land must be cultivated at just the right moment. Some say there are really only a few days during the year when clay is not too wet and not too dry to be worked and, further, irreparable harm can be done if the harvest season is wet. Cereals are anyway exhaustive crops, in that they are generally sold off farm; they are also labour-intensive at peak periods, they usually require quite a heavy investment in machinery, and they tend to encourage weeds and crop diseases so that many cereal farms rely on chemicals to keep the crops clean. Of course, on a small scale good husbandry could solve the weed and pest problem, but on a small scale the necessary machinery would be grossly underused and it can only be economically done with animal power, or even by hand if you have more time and energy than money.

Potatoes and *roots* are good crops for cleaning the land and can be important cash crops. They require quite a high level of labour at several stages of the growth cycle and they draw heavily on the soil's nutrients, which must be well replenished with FYM or fertilisers. These crops prefer the deeper loams of the Midlands and eastern counties, though carrots do best on light soils.

Pulses, on the other hand, can build up nitrogen by fixing it with the help of bacteria on their root nodules and are useful break crops on a cereal farm.

Forage crops are bulky livestock feeds, fed either in the field or in the farmyard: the crops can be growing, freshly cut or conserved as hay and silage. *Restoratives* are forage crops which recycle nutrients and organic matter within the holding because they are fed to livestock in the field. On smallholdings in particular, where climate and soil happen to be suitable, restorative and other forage crops make a great deal of sense: they can provide an even cheaper source of energy than grass and they need relatively low levels of soil nutrients. Indeed, they are more suitable for small-scale farming: larger and more intensively stocked units will produce far too much manure and the land could become overwhelmed, with a serious risk of run-off and thus pollution of the watercourses. William Cobbett, in *Cottage Economy*, advised how the owner of a cow could feed her all year round on crops grown on a mere 40 rods of land — about a third of a hectare.

Typical restoratives include kale, maize, grazing leys, fodder rape, high-energy fodder beet, stubble turnips, swedes and other folded roots, but forage crops also include more interesting species such as comfrey, or mixtures such as dredge corn (barley mixed with oats) or mashlum (cereals with peas and beans, often for silage). They are also useful as break crops, or as pioneer crops when old pasture needs renewing: they help to break down old turf and leave a better seedbed for re-sowing the ley. They can also be used as game cover in the meantime, if that is your interest.

In the mid 19th century a small farmer on a mixed farm might grow a continuous supply of green food throughout the year thus on five acres: put down half an acre to lucerne, then in May sow one sixth of the remaining land with vetches and one sixth with forage rape (the brassica, not the oilseed); in June, one fourth to turnips and one sixth to swedes, with one fourth to mangold wurzels transplanted during the month; in September sow one fourth with rye and one fourth with vetches (before the turnips) and one sixth Italian ryegrass (before swedes). This, apparently, should leave half an acre for early cabbage, transplanted in September and followed by late cabbage. The mathematics is confusing, to say the least, but the *Agricultural Gazette* of 1854 did not seek to make life easy!

Cropping systems

Ideally, different types of crop are grown in *rotation* to avoid the build-up of problems specific to each group. The old Norfolk rotation, for example, began with root crops which were folded by sheep in winter (*folding* is the invaluable practice of putting livestock — usually sheep — on to a limited area so that they can manure and tread the land while they graze the crop) followed by a spring barley cash crop undersown with a red clover ley which was grazed in spring and summer, and finally a winter wheat cash crop. Although the basic principles of a sequence of different types of crop to break pest cycles and restore fertility to the land still hold good, to be really effective such systems depend on the availability of livestock. Even arable farms today will often bring in sheep or cattle in the spring to graze winter-sown cereals and encourage tillering (the production of sideshoots), with the bonus of their manure. This is only a step away from arable folding, which used to be widespread and which, for example, gave impetus to the development of sheep breeds such as the Southdown, a type which originally grazed the chalk downs (contributing vitally to their ecology) and was eagerly welcomed by arable farmers in the adjacent Wealden claylands, for whom sheep-folding was an essential part of crop rotation, giving much-needed manure to their fields.

A variation on the rotation theme is *catch-cropping*, e.g. growing an extra crop between a cereal harvest and a spring-sown cereal. A typical mixed holding running some sheep or dairy cows, for example, can certainly find a use for quick-growing forage grown as a catchcrop between two main crops, perhaps direct-drilled into the autumn stubble, or undersown with the first crop to be grazed off or made into silage.

Another feature of many rotations in the past — and beginning to find a role again today — is the practice of *fallowing*, which is not merely leaving the land to its own devices to become a glorious hotchpotch of weeds but is carefully managed by periodical cultivation throughout the growing season so that weeds are encouraged to germinate and can be eradicated by a combination of disturbance and the drying out which accompanies frequent working of the soil. Modern farmers have forgotten the art of managing fallow land and would do well to consult their grandfathers before it is too late.

Harvesting

The *yield* of a cereal crop depends on a combination of the number of grains in each head and the individual size and weight of those grains. Crop weight is also affected by the *moisture content* of the crop, and a yield which owes its heaviness to a high moisture content is not desirable: a damp crop will rot or ferment in store. Drying can be an expensive operation and the aim is to harvest at the optimum moment when the yield is at a maximum and the crop is ripe and dry enough not to need too much artificial drying, but before it is at the stage of shedding the grains on the field as it is harvested (which would give birds, rodents and other gleaners a feast at your expense).

An occasional cereal harvest problem is *lodging*: the crop is laid flat on the ground by wind or heavy rain. If the crop stems are still green when this happens, they often bend themselves upwards again at a node and continue to grow, usually with reduced yields. If the crop lodges when it is nearly ripe, the grain can be spoilt on the ground and harvesting is more awkward. There are two main factors in lodging: either the crop is in an exposed setting, or the straw is intrinsically weak, perhaps genetically, or as a result of shading, disease or too much nitrogen in the soil.

Although harvesting is now fully mechanised, there are situations in which older practices might be followed, including field drying, stacking and threshing. It is many years since I have been *stooking*, for example: it used to be the way of allowing the crop to dry naturally before it was stacked, and is still useful if an old *binder* has been used rather than a combine harvester. For a binder, wheat is ready to harvest when the grain feels firm but not hard between finger and thumb and the straw is yellow all the way up: left any later, it will shed when cut. Oats for the binder are cut rather immature, with a trace of green still in the straw (which at that stage still has good feed value as a supplement for hay), but barley must be completely ripe, with its heads hanging down and no colour left in the straw at all.

A binder leaves the crop with the grain intact on the straw in bound sheaves, ready to be stooked by hand in the field. The sheaves can be lifted by their bands but should then be carried under the arm to the nearest stook position, two at a time. Here they are dropped with a bump, butts on the ground, so that the heads of separate sheaves interlock. The middle pairs stand almost upright but the end pairs lean inwards slightly for stability — usually four pairs to each stook. The corn remains stooked in the field to dry naturally, and the process cannot be hurried: a week for barley, a fortnight for wheat and three weeks for oats, they used to say — and that was the *minimum*, and in fine weather. Of course the process takes much longer in a wet season, and if rain does wet the stooks the sheaves can be turned round as soon as the outsides are dry enough to face inwards. To test when the crop is dry enough, thrust your hand well into some of the sheaves, beneath the bands — which is the last part to dry (along with the butts). Do not cart the crop until these parts feel crisp and dampfree.

Next comes *stacking*, in which the sheaves are piled in such a way that the grain is protected from the weather, heads to the centre and butt ends all facing outwards with a slight downward trend to shed the rain. Start by building a round stook of up to eight sheaves at the centre and lay other sheaves closely to them all the way round; continue circling like this and make the sheaves slope more and more as you go so that those in the outside ring are practically horizontal. Now for the second layer or course: start at the circumference rather than the middle this time and put down a close-packed ring of sheaves right on top of the outside ring of the first course and work towards the middle. Thereafter all courses are laid starting at the centre and working outwards, making quite sure that the centre of the stack is always domed because stacks inevitably sink in the middle later and will eventually form a dip so that the straw would point downwards to the centre, funnelling the rain to the heart of the stack. The diameter of a circular rick would be 5–6 yards for an average old-fashioned crop on 5–6 acres. Or the same acreage could give an oblong stack five yards long and four yards wide, in which shape the corners (as well as the centre) should be kept higher than the sides.

Then comes the roof, formed by gradually drawing in each successive course to make a firm, steep slope. Finish it off with a thick layer of straw in a tightly packed ridge or crest, and then thatch it with good wheat straw in the manner described later for haystacks.

Very occasionally the weather is dry and warm enough to allow threshing straight from the stook, avoiding all the bother of making a stack, but in a particularly wet season adequate ripening might take some weeks or even months in the stack.

With a combine harvester, of course, all the threshing is done as the crop is cut: the machine takes in the whole crop at one end and separates it into straw, grain and chaff, leaving the straw behind it in windrows and storing the grain until enough has been accumulated to discharge into an attendant tractor-drawn trailer for carting to the grain-store. Magic! What would the ghosts of farmers past think of it all?

Straw

Until very recently, many farmers burned their straw in the field, partly to get rid of a bulky 'waste' material and partly to clean the land for the next crop. But smallholders will quickly appreciate that straw is a most valuable commodity, either for returning to the soil after it has been chopped to provide OM and improve soil structure, or baled for livestock litter or bulk feed, or for conversion into a wide range of manufactured products from insulation materials, thatch and paper to fuel and starch.

Grassland

Grass is Britain's natural crop — and it *is* a crop, which should be nurtured as such, even if it is uncultivated rough grazing. The aim in managing grassland is to ensure that you make the most of what it can offer: it can be the cheapest feed on the holding.

The main types of grassland are:

★ Rough upland (natural vegetation, mainly for summer grazing)
★ Lowland heath (heather, moorland grasses)
★ Southern chalk downlands (mainly sheep's fescue, red fescue and herbs)
★ Fens
★ Enclosed permanent pasture (at least five years old, with wide quality range)
★ Temporary grass/clover leys (up to five years old, usually within an arable rotation)

Grassland plants

The main constituents of grassland are grasses, legumes (clovers, lucerne, sainfoin) and herbs.

Grasses

There are perhaps 150 varieties of grass in Britain: they include numerous wild species and also many cultivated strains, each with their own characteristics. Some are 'early bite' grasses; some grow early in the season and develop more stem growth for hay; others are more leafy for longer-term grazing; some are best for temporary leys and others for permanent pasture. Smallholders would probably do best to concentrate on permanent pasture, creating a really good mixture of plants for the sake of their animals' palates and health as well as for continuity of good grazing throughout the season and the ability of the sward to withstand grazing pressure. Seek the advice of local farmers and local seed merchants about the most appropriate grass mixtures for your area and never be persuaded to sow just a single variety. With a mixture (including different grasses as well as clover and herbs) you should be assured of a good spread of growth throughout the season rather than an overwhelming flush followed by a dearth, and you should also find that at least something will survive climatic extremes of drought or flooding or heat or cold and will defy the ravages of monoculture diseases and pests — all this quite apart from tickling the palate of your animals and giving them a better balance of minerals in that different varieties will take up and release soil minerals in different proportions. However, if your interest is solely in cutting for hay or silage, management will be simpler if the mix is of varieties with similar flowering times.

The main agricultural grasses include:
★ Short-duration ryegrasses (for example Italian, with a life of 18-30 months)
★ Perennial ryegrasses (the basis of most long leys but not good in exceptionally hot or very cold seasons)
★ Cocksfoot (deep-rooting native which can withstand drought)
★ Timothy (persistent, hardy and palatable but modest)
★ Meadow fescue (high digestibility, very adaptable)

Appendix 6 describes the major grasses and their qualities.

Legumes

Legumes have root nodules which provide a home for particular bacteria able to fix atmospheric nitrogen, making it available to the host plant. The group includes red and white clovers, alsike, annual trifolium, trefoil, lucerne and sainfoin.

Clovers are important in longterm grazing: they knit the sward, fix nitrogen, persist in times of drought, have a high feed value and are palatable, but beware of the possibility of bloat (a condition in which a ruminant is unable to release stomach gases and literally expands like a balloon). Clovers can also be grown in temporary leys for hay and silage. Reds are short-lived but useful and are often grown 'straight' (i.e. as a single-species crop); whites are the heart of grazing leys, more persistent than reds though less productive, and are classified by their leaf size. Alsike is often mixed with red clover, while trifolium is usually sown into cereal stubbles to provide an abundance of greenstuff the following May, and trefoil has a similar role on thin chalk soils.

Lucerne (known also as alfalfa) stretches its amazing roots halfway to Australia and is ideal in dry areas; it can give very high yields when cut for silage or barn-dried hay but is not grazed: it is not particularly palatable or digestible, though members of the lucerne family can boost butterfat yields in dairy animals. It has a high protein content and is increasingly popular with horse and goat owners. An Essex farmers' co-operative has more or less cornered the market in growing alfalfa for some 25 years now: the Dengie Crops group invested in very expensive high-temperature dryers which run non-stop from May to August to deal with the three or four cuts a year taken by the co-operative's growers. The lucerne is dried from 70 per cent moisture content down to 30 per cent in a matter of seconds and is sold as pellets or precision-chopped with molasses, or in concentrate mixes with straw. This highspeed drying reduces the considerable problem of leaf shedding during lucerne haymaking and the fermentation problems in the silage, which can lead to bloat in the animals that eat it.

Sainfoin (also known as cockshead or holy grass) used to be widely grown on calcareous soils and shares many of the qualities of lucerne, though its yields are lower. It needs light, dry, well-limed soils (pH 6.5) and a southern warmth: it is hopeless on cold wet land. Some varieties can persist for many years, but it is sometimes difficult to establish if it has competition from weeds.

Vetches or tares are also legumes producing a high volume of greenstuff rich in protein but the seed is rather expensive.

Grassland herbs

Herbs can be invaluable in permanent pasture: they add variety to the menu, they are generally deep-rooting and therefore resilient and they also provide a good supply of minerals. In addition, many herbs contribute directly to the good health of livestock and the best way of feeding medicinal herbs is by seeding them into permanent pasture or perhaps as 'hedgerow leys' on a sunny bank from which the animals can help themselves. Learn to value 'weeds'!

There are some excellent handbooks on the use of herbs for livestock which give comprehensive details of the large number of different species and their qualities. Every region has its own natural herbs (farm sprays permitting) but perhaps the most useful in pasture are burnet, chicory, yarrow, rib grass, borage, comfrey, tansy and the typical garden herbs (rosemary, marjoram, sage, dill, fennel, aniseed and so on). However, beware of herbs which can taint dairy products, and also make absolutely certain that none of your pasture or hedgerow plants are poisonous to livestock (see Appendix 7). If you have pregnant animals, give them access to wild raspberry leaves (or blackberry or briar rose, which are less effective) and if your animals are in milk let them have access to milkwort, speedwell, comfrey and various aromatic herbs to increase yield. Offer crushed nettles, watercress and watermint to freshly calved cows; also let cows have access to hedgerow tonics such as hawthorn, hazel, bramble, wild rose, elder and willow (the latter much loved by browsing goats) and pasture tonics such as herb-robert, cranesbill and, for dry cows, ground-ivy.

Many horses are kept in paddocks which are thoroughly horse-sick from constant grazing and the build-up of worms is even worse than the more visible armies of ragwort, dock and thistle. The grass itself has usually lost its useful herbs, including those which could help expel internal parasites — mustard, wild turnip and couch grass, for example, or hedgerow remedies such as ash twigs, elder, broom tips and brambles.

Mustard, incidentally, is a useful quick-growing crop for disinfecting a poultry run if it is dug in as green manure with a little soot and salt. In the field, poultry appreciate plants like chickweed, cleavers (or goosegrass — appreciated by turkeys as well as geese, and turkeys also do well on lucerne and red clover), dandelion, wormwood, fennel (these last three are excellent tonics), clover, comfrey, groundsel, nettles and rue. Rue, garlic and vervain are good worm preventatives and useful for immunising birds against infectious diseases; spurry and dried nettles are good fattening foods; while as general conditioners let your birds have access to cresses, vetches, marigold and the garden aromatics like thyme, sage and marjoram as well as the pasture plants already mentioned.

Comfrey and chicory

Chicory is a very pretty plant with its attractive blue flowers; its leaves are a good cattle tonic when it is planted in a grazing ley and its deep roots are useful to the soil. I once converted a two-acre cereal stubble into a housecow paddock and had the bonus of chicory which had been established on the headland as pheasant cover — delightful!

Chicory is a pasture plant, and also grows on wasteland. Comfrey, on the other hand, likes moisture and thrives by ditches and other damp places. It, too, is attractive in flower, with hanging clusters of pink, blue or cream bells, and in some countries and some periods it has been grown widely as a fodder plant. It also has important medicinal properties, and its roots make excellent spring tonics for cattle and horses. Its main medicinal role is betrayed by its alternative name, knit-bone.

Comfrey introduced from the Caucasus was being grown in Britain early in the 19th century as a gigantic ornamental plant and was soon being regarded as a useful agricultural crop as a greenfood for cattle, sheep and lambs. It became very popular with smallholders and farmers in the 1950s, when it was claimed that in the right conditions Russian comfrey could yield as much as 100 tons of silage to the acre (compared then to the seven tons of grass silage). It is rich in protein, grows very quickly, can produce 20–30 tons in its first year and considerably more in subsequent years, and seems to thrive on frequent cutting. It is fed as hay or silage rather than grazed. The soil should be fertile and fairly deep; it will do well on clay but not on chalk.

Pasture management

Grass is the natural food and major source of energy and protein for ruminants (though goats prefer to browse) and it is also quite a complex one. If you are serious about your animals, look more deeply into the subject of grass as a food and learn about how the different stages of growth affect its nutritional qualities. Some useful publications are mentioned in the Bibliography.

Grass is not consistent. It not only grows at varying rates according to the season but its feeding value also fluctuates. For example,

although the diagram shows that there are two peak growth rates (spring and late summer), the nutritional value of the second flush is much less than that of earlier grass and you can have a situation of fill-belly but inadequate nutrition. Likewise, an early cut of hay might not yield nearly as much bulk as a later cut but, ounce for ounce, it will be more nutritious.

By way of example, if you took a first cut of perennial ryegrass on 20th May you might achieve more than 4t/ha of dry matter then and there, with a regrowth giving a second cut on 20th July of 5.5t/ha; but in the same conditions a first cut delayed until 20th June might yield nearly 8t/ha but would only yield 1.1t/ha on a second cut on 20th July. The total yield from two cuts will be a little less in weight in the second example and you will find that the nutritional quality of the later first cut is less than that of the lower yielding early cut: you have to feed more of it for the same results.

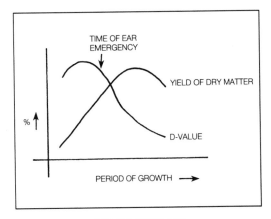

VALUE OF GRASS

(a) Digestibility

D-value (Digestibility) = percentage of organic dry matter which can be digested by animal. ME (Metabolisable Energy) = energy available to animal for body maintenance and production
$0.15D = ME$

Digestibility and protein

The value of grass can be measured in terms of its protein content and its *D-value* or digestibility factor (the digestible organic matter as a percentage of the dry matter in

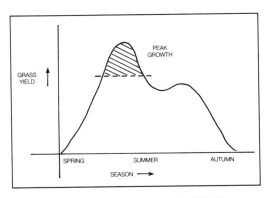

SEASONAL GRASSLAND GROWTH

The excess during the peak growth period in early summer can be cut for conservation as hay or silage.

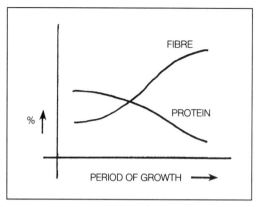

(b) Protein

the material) which represents the percentage that is actually digested from what has been eaten and which has a direct relationship with the useful or metabolisable energy (ME) the animal can obtain from its food (ME = 0.15D). The bulk is measured in terms of its fibre content and its proportion of dry matter. The Figures show how these factors vary seasonably and the conserver's aim is to cut the crop at the optimum moment when digestibility and protein levels are high but before the fibre content is too great. Because of the nature of the two conservation processes, the fibre content of hay will be higher than that of silage at the time the crop is cut. Digestibility falls at a rate of a third to a half of a D-value unit per day once seedheads have formed, and it should be noted that different species or varieties reach their optimum levels at different times in the season.

Growth patterns

Consider a typical plant of perennial ryegrass, the main constituent of many permanent pastures. Except when it is actively producing a seedhead, the plant's active growth region is near ground level and below grazing or cutting height. The youngest area of a leaf is at its base, pushing the older growth upwards ahead of it as the leaf cells grow. Growth of the whole plant can also be lateral, by means of 'tillering'. A tiller is an aerial shoot arising from a leaf axil, and the more tillers there are, the more branched the plant becomes. The tillers can develop individual

root systems and effectively become self-sufficient, spreading over the field surface to thicken the sward. Each tiller has the potential to develop further tillers and to produce a flowering stem. However, when these stems are triggered into growth by the pattern of daylength and temperature, fresh tiller development is suppressed and the plant concentrates its resources on the production of fast-growing stems so that the developing flowerhead or ear is carried well above the surface of the field into the light and ready to catch the breeze for pollination. Such an ear is the apex of the stem and when the stem is defoliated it becomes incapable of regrowth. Once the ears are visible, vegetative growth is greatly reduced and the longer the ears remain on the plant, the slower the subsequent development of vegetative organs: tillers remaining after a crop of ears on tall stems are slow to regrow. But if the plant's vegetative growth (i.e. leaves) is thereafter removed frequently, the sward will thicken again as tillering increases.

If you cut your hay or silage late in order to try to get a higher yield, you could delay the rate of regrowth quite seriously. If you frequently defoliate the grass in spring (a time of rapid tiller development before it is suppressed by stem growth between May/June and the autumn) you will increase the density of the sward because ear development is restricted and therefore tiller formation is continued, as long as the new leaf growth is not nipped off the moment it shows a timid tip. You will also encourage the tillering species at the expense of some of the 'weed' grasses which do not tiller so freely.

Top dressing

Nitrogen is the key to maximum grass production, if that is what you seek. The Germans, during the First World War, developed intensive grassland management based on the use of large quantities of nitrogen, as they badly needed abundant grass to boost low stocks of animal feedstuffs, and the system came to Britain in 1926. Phosphorus and potassium (P and K) help to establish a sward and maintain its vigour, but do not apply potash in the spring if you are grazing livestock — it will reduce the availability of magnesium in the plants and you run the risk of the animals suffering from staggers. Lime the field if it is too acid, remembering that legumes in particular are very sensitive to low pH values. On stands set aside for hay or silage, you can spread FYM in spring or slurry in summer.

Harrowing and rolling

In early spring (and in autumn if conditions permit) harrow grazed fields to spread the dung and molehills, pull out dead herbage, aerate the soil and freshen the grass. Roll it, too, in early spring, especially if cattle have poached the land during the winter, and dress it if necessary. Mind you, there are those who say that the only good which a chain-harrow does is to exercise the horse that pulls it.

Pasture improvement

If you need to improve existing pasture, you need to identify the reasons for its degeneration before deciding on the best methods of improvement. You cannot change the climate but you can improve several other factors which affect the quality of grassland, especially acidity, drainage and soil nutrients. You can also ensure that grass is maintained at the best height for a given situation, either by grazing management or by mowing. It might be simply that the stocking rate has been too high — or too low or erratic; or that the soil lacks nutrients or has become too acid, or, very probably, that the drainage is poor.

The main methods of improvement are: a gradual process of rejuvenation, dealing with drainage, soil fertility and acidity, and practising a better regime of grazing and cutting; a quicker and more expensive process of renovation involving the introduction of new species into the existing pasture, by direct drilling or slit seeding, or by the more haphazard method of simply scattering seed when the soil surface is moist and then relying on sheep to tread the seeds for two or three days; and the more radical and even more expensive alternative of starting again, destroying the original cover by ploughing (or chemically) and reseeding the whole field from scratch.

So, for poor and rather unproductive pasture: test for acidity (and lime if necessary); check the drainage (mole-drain if necessary); and above all, perhaps, check for matting. Very often you will find that a fibrous layer of dead and decaying grasses is swamping finer grasses but allowing coarser ones to flourish. Give the field a good harrowing. Once it has been raked about, the matted fibre should gradually rot down to humus. In early spring, use chain harrows to level the ground and then give it a good roll. Put stock in for the summer and apply top dressings in the autumn or spring if necessary. Sometimes it is in fact better to plough out the pasture completely and take off an arable crop or two before reseeding.

Sowing grass

Grass can be undersown with an early-harvest, short-straw nurse crop (probably spring barley or perhaps forage peas), which is either harvested as usual or cut as whole-crop silage, green grain included. Sow the grass mixture immediately after the cereal has been sown, preferably in March, or delay sowing the grass until the cereal crop is well established. However, there is bound to be competition between grass and cereal in the early stages. Alternatively, the grass mixture can be sown without a nurse crop, preferably in spring (mid-March to end of April) or late summer; graze it quite early to encourage tillering, though not if it was sown as late as September.

The seed can be broadcast or drilled, or direct-drilled after killing off the previous crop, or you can renovate a sward by slit-seeding into the existing cover without any previous cultivation apart from clearing weeds aggressive enough to swamp the new grass seedlings — but make sure that problems such as poor drainage or acidity, which might have caused the old sward to deteriorate originally, have been remedied. The scatter-and-tread technique mentioned earlier is best confined to filling up worn areas in paddocks and needs a fortnight of moist (but not wet) weather after sowing. Take care if you are broadcasting through existing herbage of any kind: wait until the dew is off the vegetation to make sure the seed doesn't simply stick to the plants.

Whatever sowing technique you use, look for a moist bed and some warmth in the soil to encourage the young plants to become established quickly. If cultivation is involved, aim for a firm bed and a fine tilth, and sow the seed shallowly — it is very fine. Drilling is better in dry regions, but where soil moisture is ample try broadcasting on a surface which has been prepared with a rib-roller and use an appropriately set fertiliser distributor to spread the seed. The rib-roller (see Machinery section) leaves an ideal corrugated surface for seed-sowing, and a very light harrowing afterwards across the ribs is all that is needed to settle the seed without burying it so deep that it fails to germinate.

Broadcasting by hand can be done with the aid of a 'fiddle', which gives a farflung and very even spread if you walk straight across the field, or you can be even more basic and sling the seed in a pouch or basket around your waist, then simply cast handfuls with a rhythmic swing of your arm from side to side across the body as you walk — very biblical, very pleasant work on a fine day, and perfectly feasible on a small acreage if you set up markers to remind you where you have already sown. In the traditional manner the crop sower would measure out the field and then measure out the seed into sacks, which were set out at appropriate intervals on the headlands. To set the sowing rate, he would walk smoothly with a steady, easy, swinging step in a straight line (perhaps in a furrow) and work out how many steps should accompany each handful of broadcast seed — perhaps two handfuls to each side for every fifteen paces, but the rhythm depended upon the type of seed and the width and depth of the furrow. Once established, the rhythm must be retained for the whole field: if some areas of it require a lighter or heavier spread, the size of the handful is adjusted rather than the stride. Of course, seed broadcast on ridges (even those as small as rib-roller patterns) will slip into the furrows. Some people sow one-handed from a sowing-cloth, usually casting only to one side; others use a basket and sow with both hands, alternately left and right; others use the cross-body swing, which is likely to be more patchy.

Your supplier will recommend appropriate seeding rates, which are usually at least 4 kg/ha for most grasses or 2 kg/ha for clover. After sowing, roll the field, then tell the birds to go elsewhere for a while, and pray that the summer is not a total drought or you will have nothing green except clover.

Grazing

It is almost impossible to suggest how many animals can be stocked on a given acreage of grassland: the variables are too many and include climate, season, the adequacy of the grazing, the species and age of the stock, production demands, the availability of other feeds — and so on. In theory, the appetite of a ruminant on grass is assessable in terms of what is known as a 'cow equivalent' (CE): the mathematical formula, if you want to know, is:

Dry matter intake (in kg/day) = 0.32 + (0.0234 × liveweight of animal in kg)

The standard cow in this equation is a Friesian weighing 550 kg. Roughly speaking, the CE of a Jersey might be about 0.6, that of a 200 kg heifer 0.38, that of a 100 kg steer 0.2 and that of a 40 kg sheep 0.1. However, ewes and suckler cows apparently eat less than expected, and the CE of a 40 kg ewe is only 0.08, or of a 550 kg beef cow 0.75. Now all you need is to estimate the weight of growing grass, its proportion of dry matter, its nutritional value . . .

Stocking rates are also affected by how much land is set aside for grass conservation as hay and silage, how wet it is and how readily poached, and how much scope there is for moving to fresh grazing. Very broadly, on reasonable lowland pasture allow an acre (or half a hectare) for a dairy cow the size of a Friesian — this should give enough for seasonal grazing and for making hay or silage to see her through a fair winter. Four Jersey cows might need as much land as three Friesians, while you could accommodate three Dexters instead of two Friesians. Beef cattle should be stocked according to their changing weight as well as to the rate of grass growth, with the aim of keeping the grass to a height of perhaps 7–9 cm, and initially at the spring turnout you could allow 1,000 kg of cattle liveweight per hectare (400 kg/acre), increasing it to 2,500 kg/ha (1,000 kg/acre) as the animals and the grass grow.

In commercial flocks, target stocking rates for breeding ewes range from 9/ha on uplands to 15.5/ha for lowland early fat lamb. In theory, you could allow nine breeding ewes (at 70 kg liveweight each) and their lambs (at an average of 1.8 lambs per ewe) to an acre of poor grazing per annum, or up to thirteen such ewes on very good grass, but remember that lambs, like beef cattle, are growing and will be eating more and more grass as their milk consumption decreases.

In the case of outdoor pigs, stock at seven or eight sows per acre at the most and do not run them on the same piece of land for more than two years consecutively. Apparently long, narrow paddocks are best for pigs: they will make a mess of one end but leave the other two-thirds as grass. (If the soil is sandy, ring the sows to protect the grass cover.)

Grazing systems

A major part of grassland management is to maintain the vegetation within the capacity of the grazers, or to increase or decrease stocking rates according to the amount and quality of the grass. That is easier said than done. In spring, the stuff grows so fast that the animals cannot keep pace with it; during the summer it slows down, spurting a little again for the late summer flush, while in winter it does not grow at all and has very little feed value anyway. The spring growth is the most nutritious.

The secret is to move stock around the holding in a calculated manner, and to preserve the excesses of flush growth for use as hay or silage in the lean months. In the meantime, keep the grass topped to grazing heights appropriate to the type of livestock.

The goodness is in the young leaf, not the old stem. Broadly, the ideal grazing height for cattle on continuous grazing is about 10 cm and for sheep 4–6 cm.

Each species has very different ways of eating. Cattle are usually quite selective and need a longer sward because they wrap their tongues around the grass and pull to tear it: they have no top incisors to cut it with. Sheep prefer short grass: they nibble it down well but tend to avoid coarse or less attractive grasses unless they have no option; if they are kept quite tight and moved regularly to a fresh piece, they will leave a tidy sward. Horses have very strong teeth and will bite the grass right down almost to the soil: like sheep, they prefer shorter grass but they are not tidy grazers as they leave rank areas untouched, especially in those parts of the field that they habitually dung.

The first choice in grazing systems lies between permanent pasture or temporary leys (where 'temporary' means up to five years). *Permanent grassland* builds up a good sward and a root system able to sustain it during periods of drought or severe winters; it also tends to contain a good mixture of plant species and thus an extended growing period as the different species mature at different times. It must be managed sensibly to be kept healthy. *Temporary leys* remind you that grass does indeed need management; they also give greater flexibility in that you can exercise choice over which plant species will be grown to suit certain purposes such as cutting for silage or hay.

The older practices of avoiding mono-stocking were based on very good sense and were directly or indirectly connected to the control of worm infestations. These internal parasites tend to be host specific: the type of worm that uses a sheep in its lifecycle is less likely to use cattle, and the mainspring of parasite control is to break the cycle by denying access to the host at crucial times. This can be done either by leaving the field unstocked for an adequate period (and longer than you think) or by stocking it with different species. In the case of young animals, especially those which are not reared by their own mothers, the problem of worms can be considerable and they must always be given clean grazing, on which there have been no adults of their kind for at least a season.

It makes sense to stock with one type of animal one season and another the following to break the parasite cycle. It is also important to offer the best grazing to the most 'important' livestock first, whether that be dairy cows for the milk cheque or youngstock for a good start in life. Sheep, incidentally, are good scavengers to clean up after other stock, though ewes need to be flushed on better grazing and lambs do need fresh land if there is any possibility of a build-up of worms.

In Australia it used to be said that horses would refuse to graze after cattle. Some ruminants will not graze after heavy manuring by geese or pigs, and most horses have a decided aversion to the presence of pigs anyway, though it all rather depends on past experience.

Mixed stocking, combining different livestock species in the same field at the same time, is perfectly feasible and often beneficial to the pasture, in that, because of different eating habits, they make a much tidier job of the sward. Cattle and reasonably amenable breeds of sheep are quite happy in the same field but, if stocking rates were too heavy, ultimately the cattle would suffer because the sheep nibble so close to the ground that they have the advantage on tightly grazed pasture.

Cattle and horses can also be mixed, though some have personal animosities. Be careful with donkeys: they can become rather possessive about their habitual field and could bully smaller livestock put with them unless the introductions are made carefully. Of course, many a racehorse has a donkey for company in the field and a goat as a stable companion. Goats can be awkward in mixed situations if they are horned but mainly because of the fencing needs; however, they can do an excellent job of improving upland grazing to the benefit of following sheep, as the goats will take the coarser stuff and encourage finer grasses for the sheep. Be a little careful of mixing lambs with goatlings because of misleading body language: a kid means it when it butts, and could give an unsuspecting lamb quite a surprise. Weaned lambs are happy enough grazing with free-range poultry.

The main grazing systems, regardless of the type of stock, are very broadly divided between extensive or intensive, and permanent or rotational. The principles are applicable to any size of livestock holding. The intensive system developed by the Germans more than seventy years ago is based on the principle that young grass is highly nutritious, and if it is maintained in a closely cropped condition it will carry larger numbers of animals. To succeed, such a system needs a lot of fertiliser and careful control of how many animals graze which area when. There is no point fertilising for extra grass if you do not use the stuff.

Set-stocking is an extensive system in which more or less the same animals are grazed over the same area throughout the season. The stocking rates must be low though the sward is likely anyway to suffer from being undergrazed in spring and overgrazed later in the year. But it does save on fencing (you only need an outer boundary) and on time spent in moving animals, and it is a traditional system for finishing beef cattle by leaving them in the same field all season at 2.5 bullocks/ha. It is also quite a natural system in terms of animal behaviour: most wild ruminants wander to find their own fresh grazing when they need it or when social circumstances demand a change of scenery, and the domesticants can exercise their natural behaviour patterns to some extent on set-stocking as long as the total area available to them is large enough and the landscape varied.

Continuous grazing is in effect set-stocking for shorter periods — say two or three months, and usually at high stocking rates with the use of plenty of N or supplementary feeding if necessary. A particular area might indeed be grazed continuously but the stocking rate is not fixed, nor are the same animals necessarily on the same patch throughout. For finishing beef animals, for example, you can take account of the growing beasts'

Understocked pasture which has grown away from the cattle: it should have been topped during the season.

growing capacity for food and reduce the stocking rate from perhaps 11/ha to 4/ha during the season.

The two-sward system at its simplest is the division of an area into two parts, one for grazing and the other for conservation. Naturally, the size of the areas can be varied according to the season so that the grazing area is less during the spring flush but can be increased later to give the animals access to aftermath in the conservation area.

Rotational grazing involves the partitioning of large areas into smaller ones and moving the animals from one to another on a regular basis. This can mean using electric fencing to give a fresh area of grazing every day or two (*strip-grazing* — often with a back fence as well to keep them off the previously grazed area — efficient but laborious, and there is often a problem of poaching along the fence line) or a more permanent division of all the holding's grazing into *paddocks*, each of which is grazed methodically for a day and then rested so that in a typical system of 21 to 28 such paddocks, each area is revisited three to four weeks later when it has had a chance to grow again. Fencing costs for the paddock system will be rather high.

Dairy cattle respond well to rotational grazing: they are used to contact with people anyway and rather enjoy fresh pasture every day, though protective suckler cows might resent the disturbance and the need to re-establish territory. Fattening cattle often seem to scour and lose weight in intensive grazing systems; they become too unsettled and are better in a more extensive system. The same applies to sheep: if you keep disturbing them you reduce their grazing time and they, too, can start scouring and losing weight. You might also cause distress and even injury if your attentions cause any panic. It depends on the type or breed of sheep and also on their relationship with you.

Suckler herds and ewes with lambs could benefit from paddock *creep systems* that allow youngsters access to fresh, wormfree grazing ahead of their mothers. It has often been said that a sheep's worst enemy is another sheep, mainly because of the problem of parasites, so do not overstock sheep unless you are prepared to drench them against worms on a regular basis. However, too low a stocking rate will actually discourage lambs from creep-grazing: the paddock needs to be bare enough to force the lambs to look for fresh grazing beyond the creep gate. In a forward-creep system, the ewes follow on to the lambs' paddock and graze it off if the lambs have failed to clear it. In any creep system for lambs, make sure that the creep gates are not more than 50m apart along the fence-line. Creeps are easily devised: set a rail which the lambs can wander under but which is too low for the ewes, or use a pair of posts too close together for older animals to pass through.

Zero grazing is an intensive system whereby animals are housed or closely yarded and their grass is cut and brought to them: they never actually go on the pasture. It is a labour-intensive system but can be useful where the pasture is too easily damaged by stock or is too far away for the easy movement of animals. It might be good for the pasture but how very boring for the animals — and what a lot of slurry.

Conservation

In winter, the feed value of grass is very low but in spring the nutrition values are at their best and the stuff grows so fast that grazing animals cannot keep up with it. Don't waste it: conserve it! Hay-making is the field equivalent of bottling fruit or making cheese: it is taking advantage of an excess in times of plenty by conserving it for use in times of need.

The earlier a crop is first cut, the better the quality of the grass but the lower its yield: you need to balance quality and yield according to your own judgement. For example, a dairy cow needs quality feeding to sustain her output but overwintered beef steers might be merely 'ticking over' as store cattle rather than growing fast and quality is

less important. But it is not only the quality of the grass at the time of cutting that counts: the efficiency of its conversion to hay or silage is a major factor in its ultimate value as a food. Once a plant is cut it continues to live for a while, using up its reserves and thus losing them to the animals which will eat the conserved matter in due course. This dissipation continues until the material is either dried or deprived of air — the former in the case of hay and the latter in silage. The degradation ceases when the moisture content is reduced to less than 15 per cent (in the field the average moisture content of a grass crop is about 80 per cent) or when the material's pH value falls below 4.2–5.0 in an oxygen-free environment. It is also possible in theory to halt degradation with chemicals or by freezing, either of which could preserve the herbage in virtually its state at the time of cutting. (How big is your deepfreeze?)

Although many large-scale farmers now prefer to make silage, many smaller farmers and horse owners keep faith with hay. Hay is convenient to handle; it has a pleasant smell (if it is well made) and a high dry-matter content so that it is concentrated goodness. Silage is a succulent substance and is usually handled mechanically and made in bulk; it has the advantage that its making does not require the minimum of three consecutive days of fine weather that is needed for hay, and can be carted from the field after a few hours of wilting. It can also be cut much earlier than hay, before the ears emerge, which means that its feeding value should be high and also that second or even third cuts will be possible and there is greater opportunity for grazing aftermaths. You might or might not manage a second hay cut in a good year.

A problem with both hay and silage for smallholders is access to the equipment needed to make them — especially silage — and many people depend on good contacts with local farmers or hire contractors. However, the smaller the crop the more likely it is that a contractor will leave it until last, and by then the crop might be past its best or the weather might have broken.

Making hay

The best hay is cut before it flowers, because it is at that stage higher in protein and starch but lower in fibre than grass in full flower. It is cut when the grass is full of growth and sap but it is harvested dry: damp hay becomes mouldy or overheated.

Hay is traditionally dried naturally in the field, with the help of sunshine and air, and the art of good haymaking is to hasten this process gently: you want to encourage the drying but without shattering the increasingly fragile leaf matter or letting its nutrients be leached away by dew or rain. It is quite possible to lose up to 20 per cent of the dry matter of the crop from rough handling between cutting it and baling the hay, and you can also lose up to a third of its protein value from leaching in the field after cutting. You want speedy drying but you must protect the leaf, which begins to be at its most vulnerable to mechanical damage when it is partially dry. The leafy part of the plant is more valuable than its stem.

In the old days the animals were turned out of the meadows in March to let the grass grow until June for the earliest cut, or until July for the very latest. The June hay was cut when the taller grasses in a mixed sward were *just* beginning to flower and well before any seed was set. They cut 'only as much as may be well overcome', or as much as could be safely dried and carried without risking losing it to wet weather. In the days when whole families helped with haymaking, the first day's cut was left in swathes which would be tossed by the women to help drying as soon as the dew had been dried off by the sun. The swathes were as wide apart as the width of a haywain.

Whether cut by scythe, horse-mower or tractor-powered mowers, it was left in swathes to dry: the grass was shaken out soon after cutting to expose a greater area for drying and was turned no more than twice in the swathe. If rain threatened, it was gathered into rows with a hay rake (at first a handheld large wooden rake, then a metal implement with a row of thirty curved tines, drawn by horse or tractor) or piled into cocks, preferably built into peaks over wooden tripods and then raked down like thatch so that the rain would be shed. Hay could only be satisfactorily cocked when it was still dry in the swathe: if it had become wet it had to be shaken out on to dry ground with handforks or a horse-drawn tedder, which consisted of two large wheels and a number of revolving iron arms and prongs which lifted and scattered the hay while the driver sat on the implement.

When the hay was dry enough, it was drawn into windrows ready for carting or sweeping towards the rick with the aid or a mechanical hay-sweep, an implement with projecting iron-shod prongs like a buckrake, mounted on the front or rear of a tractor or with two wheels so that it could be pushed by a horse. Windrowing was by a side rake or horse rake, then the sweep could quickly shift the rowed-up hay to the rick site, where an elevator helped with the work of building the stack.

If there was any doubt about whether it would overheat in the rick, it was sprinkled with salt (24–28 pounds of salt to the ton) while the stack was being built. The decision about the crop's readiness for stacking was crucial and the general rule was that it could safely be stacked when it was crisp-dry and rustled on the fork. The old saying was that it was easier to spoil hay in the rick than in the field: if it heated excessively in the stack it would at best lose its feed value and at worst spontaneously combust.

Rick-building was skilled work. First a thick layer of straw or brushwood was laid as a foundation to a size previously planned. The narrower the stack, the less likely it was to heat, and a maximum width was twelve feet. In some places ricks were built on stone floors covered with a deep layer of green bracken which, as every tramp knew, insulated against rising damp. The bracken allowed air to circulate and, if the layer was feet thick, it deterred rodents: apparently gnawing bracken (or marestail) makes a rat's mouth sore! In wet areas, wooden ventilators might be built into the stacks to let air circulate right through them.

Finally, in the days before tarpaulins, the rick was thatched with wheat straw. First of all the rick was made tight and trim, and a crown was built up by pulling any loose hay from the sides and transferring it to make a fairly steep, firm roof. About 1.5–2 tons of good straw could thatch 100 square feet of roof surface. The straw was sprinkled with water the day before to make it more pliable and able to be more closely packed, and was laid out in handy-sized lots or 'yelms', each perhaps 18 in wide and up to 2 in thick in the loose state, laid crosswise on top of each other ready to be carried up to the roof. The thatcher's equipment included a ladder, straw-roping or stout cord to hold down the thatch, plenty of 12–15 in pointed wooden spars or pegs bent or twisted like hairpins, a small hand rake, a peg-driving mallet and a pair of shears.

Thatching started at the eaves. The lower-most layer of straw was set butt-ends downwards with a good projection to throw rainwater away from the stack, but on higher layers the straw was laid heads down. Each yelm was laid with its base overlapping the top of the one below and its upper part tucked into the roof, and each yelm-wide section from eaves to crest formed a 'steltch'. At the crest of the steltch, the final yelm crossed with that on the other side of the roof to overtop the peak. Each steltch was fitted as closely as possible to its neighbour to give continuous cover.

As he worked, the thatcher used the back of his rake to beat down the thatch close and tight and its toothed side to rake the straw straight. Each steltch was secured with spars and cords: rows of spars were driven in to about half their length and 12–15 in apart, the first row about 10 in from the eaves and then a couple of rows fairly close together near the crest. The cord was threaded through the hairpin loops of the spars and pulled tight before the spars were driven home with the mallet. The final touch was to make a tidy job by trimming the thatch at the eaves and crest and raking off any loose straw.

Today, haymaking can be much simpler — though you can still do it by hand on a small acreage if you wish. Your first problem will be to find a 'personal' scythe of the right weight and balance, and your next is how to use it tirelessly. Let the scythe do the work, and take your time. Move forward slowly but steadily, swinging the scythe from right to left in a wide semicircle (oh, go on then, sing as you work!) and keep the blade parallel to the ground. To prevent a natural tendency to lift the height of the cut towards the end of each swing, lean your body forward at that point. In theory, you should leave a nice, tidy swathe to your left. Once or twice during the curing, fluff up the swathes with a wooden hayrake to expose damper areas to sun and air for drying once or twice during the curing. Use short and long pitchforks to toss the dried crop up on to the haywain for carting to the stack.

Whatever method you use, the aim is to reduce the moisture content in the field down to 25 per cent or less before the hay is ricked, trussed or, today, baled.

Modern haymaking follows the old principles, including never trying to cut more hay than you can pick up in a day if the weather changes. Once the job has started, get on with it and forget everything else until the hay is safely in. Cut it quickly and cut it when D-values are at the best — ideally at 63 but in practice about 60, usually at the time of ear emergence.

The stages are, first, the cutting, and then the drying, which can be in the field as of old, loose, or in the bale, or in the stack or in the store.

Cutting can be with a reciprocal knife mower, unless the crop is badly laid; a double-knife mower, which gives a fast cut in any conditions; a flail cutter, which helps fast drying in the field but you will lose a lot of valuable dry matter from shattering; or a drum or disc mower, for a minimum leaf loss, fast cutting and high performance in all conditions.

Quick hay is made by conditioning the crop immediately after it is cut. A conditioner hastens the drying process by bruising the grasses to release juices, and is used in tandem with the mower. It might be a disc cutter with rotary swinging flails or tedder tines, or a drum rotary mower with steel crushing rollers. On the first day the crop is cut and then moved twice in the field: cut it, move the swath to dry the broken top layer, then immediately move it again, ideally with a tedder. On the second day, wait for the dew to lift and then move the crop again but more gently, with a turner. On the third day, turn it once or twice. You might be able to bale it on the third day in ideal conditions of weather and type of crop but wait another day or two if necessary. Do not bale prematurely: wait until the crop has dried to about 25 per cent of its fresh-cut weight if you are baling in the field, or to 35–40 per cent for barn-dried bales, or by about 30 per cent if you are using additives to hasten curing. Additives allow you to bale at higher moisture levels so that the crop is leafier: they are based on propionic acid applied evenly as a fine spray as you bale, to inhibit bacterial fermentation and suppress the growth of mould.

At 30–40 per cent moisture, the leaves begin to rustle to the touch and do not yield moisture unless they are rubbed quite hard, though the stems exude easily if you scrape them with a thumbnail or knife. At 25–30 per cent, a bundle of hay twisted in your hands yields no surface moisture and remains quite difficult to snap, whereas at 20–25 per cent it snaps easily and rustles readily, and the leaves begin to shatter. At 15–20 per cent the material is fragile in the swath and it is very difficult to extract juices, even from the stems.

Bales can either be left in the field to continue drying or you can defer baling until the total moisture content is about 23 per cent and then stack immediately in an airy barn. Bales can be standard size — which means manageable but very variable in dimension and weight — or big-bale size, in which case each bale might weight 600–900 kg and needs adequate machinery to handle it, including grippers on a tractor's front-end loader or a single spike for round bales. Big bales are more weatherproof if they are round rather than rectangular but hay in round bales must be of a lower moisture content at the time of baling. In general, big-bale hay is cured down to 25–30 per cent moisture content in the field.

Hay can also be *barn-dried*. Bales with a moisture content of 35–45 per cent are stacked tightly on edge in crossbonded layers over flat ventilated floors (welded mesh or timber suspended 60 cm above ground level) and unheated air is fanned through the floor so that it passes through (rather than between) each bale. There are other systems for drying bales with unheated air.

If you are wealthy enough, or are part or a co-operative, you could try grass-drying using a horizontal conveyor-belt system which moves the crop over hot air at about 160°C or pneumatic rotary drum driers at up to 1100°C, but these are extremely expensive — even a small mobile on-farm system would cost £50,000. The equipment can also be used to conserve wholecrop lucerne, forage rye, beans, maize and cereals.

Finally, perhaps just for the historical record, here is the Middlesex Report. Early in the 19th century it was said that the farmers of Middlesex, who supplied the metropolis with its hay, managed their haymaking in a 'very perfect manner'. This is a day-by-day account of how they did so and it gives some useful tips for the real hay perfectionist:

The Middlesex Report
'**First day.** All the grass mown before nine o'clock in the morning is tedded, in which great care is taken thoroughly to loosen every lump, and to strew it evenly over all the ground. By this regular method of tedding grass for hay, the hay will be of a more valuable quality, heats more equally in the stack, consequently not so liable to damage, or fire; will be of greater quantity when cut into trusses, and will sell at a greater price: for when the grass is suffered to lie a day or two before it is tedded out of the swath, the upper surface is dried by the sun and winds, and the interior part is not dried, but withered, so that the herbs lose much both as to quality and quantity. The next operation consists in turning it with the same degree of care and attention; and if, from the number of hands, they are able to turn the whole again, they do so, or at least

as much of it as they can, till twelve or one o'clock, at which time they dine. The first thing to be done after dinner, is to rake it into what are called single windrows. That is, they all rake in such a manner as that each person makes a row, which rows are three or four feet apart. The last operation of the day is to put it into grass-cocks.

'**Second Day.** The business of this day commences with tedding all the grass that was mown the first day *after* nine o'clock, and all that was mown this day *before* nine o'clock. Next, the grass-cocks are to be well shaken out into staddles (or separate plats) of five or six yards in diameter. If the crop should be so thin and light as to leave the spaces between these staddles rather large, such spaces must be immediately raked clean, and the rakings mixed with the other hay, in order to all its drying of an uniform colour. The next business is to turn the staddles, and after that, to turn the grass that was tedded in the first part of the morning, once or twice, in the manner described for the first day. This should all be done before twelve or one o'clock, so that the whole may lie to dry while the work-people are at dinner. After dinner, the first thing to be done is, to rake the staddles into *double* windrows; in doing which every two persons rake the hay in opposite directions, or towards each other, and by that means form a row between them of double the size of a single windrow. Each of these double windrows is about six or eight feet distant from each other. The next operation is to rake the grass into *single* windrows; then the double windrows are put into bastard-cocks; and lastly, the single windrows are put into grass-cocks. This completes the work of the second day.

'**Third Day.** The grass mown and not spread on the second day, and also that mown in the early part of this day, is first to be tedded in the morning; and then the grass-cocks are to be spread into staddles as before, and the bastard-cocks into staddles of less extent. These lesser staddles, though last spread, are first turned, then those which were in grass-cocks; and next, the grass is turned once or twice before twelve

or one o'clock, when the people go to dinner as usual. If the weather has proved sunny and fine, the hay which was last night in bastard-cocks will this afternoon be in a proper state to be carried. It seldom happens, in dry weather, but that it may be carried on the third day; but if the weather should, on the contrary, have been cool and cloudy, no part of it, probably, will be fit to carry.

'In that case the first thing set about after dinner is to rake that which was in grass-cocks last night into double windrows; then the grass which was this morning spread from the swaths, into single windrows. After this, the hay which was last night in bastard-cocks, is made up into full-sized cocks, and care taken to rake the hay up clean, and also to put the rakings upon the top of each cock. Next, the double windrows are put into bastard-cocks and the single windrows into grass-cocks, as on the preceding days.

'**Fourth day.** On this day the great cocks just mentioned are usually carried before dinner. The other operations of the day are such, and in the same order, as before described, and are continued daily, until the hay harvest is completed.

'In the course of hay-making, the grass should as much as possible be protected both day and night against rain and dew, by cocking. Care should also be taken to proportion the number of hay-makers to that of mowers, so that there may not be more grass in hand at any time than can be managed according to the described process. This proportion is about twenty hay-makers (of which number twelve may be women) to four mowers. The latter are sometimes taken half a day to assist the former. But in hot, windy, or very drying weather, a greater proportion of hay-makers will be required than when the weather is cloudy and cool. It is particularly necessary to guard against spreading more than the number of hands can get into cock the same day, or before rain. In showery and uncertain weather, the grass may sometimes be suffered to lie three, four, and even five days in the swath. But before it has lain long enough for the under side of the swath to become yellow (which, if suffered to lie long, would be case), particular care should be taken to turn the swaths with the heads of the rakes. In this state it will cure so much in about two days, as only to require being tedded a few hours, when the weather is fine, previous to its being put together and carried. In this manner hay may be made and stacked at a small expense and of good colour, but the tops and bottoms of the grass are insufficiently separated by it. If, from unforeseen circumstances, the hay has been damaged by sudden or successive rains, it will be advisable to salt the hay as it is stacked.

'There are no hay-stacks more neatly formed, or better secured, than those of Middlesex. At every vacant time, while the stack is carrying up, the men are employed in pulling it with their hands into a proper shape; and about a week after it is finished, the whole of it is properly thatched, and then secured from receiving any damage from the wind, by means of straw-rope extended along the eaves, up the ends, and near the ridge. The ends of the thatch are afterwards cut evenly below the eaves of the stack, just of sufficient length for the rain water to drip quite clear of the hay. When the stack happens to be placed in a situation which may be suspected of being too damp in the winter, a trench of about six to eight inches deep is dug round, and nearly close to it, which serves to convey all the water from the spot, and renders it perfectly dry and secure. The foregoing practice can scarcely admit of improvement, but in *wet weather*, or in those local situations where the surrounding hills cause rain to fall much more frequently than in the open country, the practice adopted by farmers in Yorkshire is well deserving of consideration. The grass is cut as low as possible, and on the day following is strewed *with the hands* in such a regular and even manner, that no lumps appear on the surface. In this part of the work, neither forks nor rakes are used, except where the grass is very light indeed. Next day, if the weather be fine, it is turned with the rake-head in a very neat and regular order; on the third day, if the weather continue fine, it is to be put into *hand* or *lap cocks*; one raker goes before a cocker; each cocker takes up about eight or ten pounds weight of hay, shakes it up very lightly, then puts one hand a little under it, and the other on the side of it, takes it up and sets it down again gently, where it is raked clean, in a neat regular row, leaving a hole about the middle in the side of the cock, so as to admit air in case of wet weather. Cocks made in this manner, it is asserted, will repel the rain, and throw it off better than any large cocks carelessly and hastily put together with the rake or fork, and are also less liable to be disturbed by wind or tempests. This mode of hay-making is affirmed on the test of nearly fifty years' experience, to be far preferable to any other. Ricks of a circular form, with a conical head, are preferable to long ricks, being less liable to injury from the weather in this than in any other shape.'

As Cobbett would say, 'What a deal of *work!*'

Making silage

Whereas hay is dried, silage is succulent. Ensilaging pickles green crops in acid: they are fermented under acidic conditions with air excluded. The aim is to encourage the right type of natural acid and in well-made silage lactic acid predominates. Acetic acid is also present, and a very little butyric acid as well. The balance between the acids is largely determined by the proportions of sugar and moisture in the crop at the time of cutting.

Sugar levels vary according to the type of crop and its stage of growth. They are low in, for example, clover or young grass but can be improved by the use of silage additives. Moisture content at picking up should be 70–75 per cent and is normally achieved by allowing the crop to wilt for a few hours after it has been cut. The drier the crop when it is picked up, the more concentrated its sugars (which helps to encourage the desirable lactobacilli), the less bulky it is to cart and the less effluent there will be in the store. For *haylage*, the moisture content would would be even lower — preferably less than 50 per cent. Haylage is silage made in a tower, and it *has* to be be drier than silage made in a clamp or pit: the cut crop is blown into the top of the tower and, by the fact of it being a tower, becomes well compacted and can make very good silage. However, if the material is very wet when the tower is loaded, there is a serious risk of corrosion to the structure and its possible collapse. Towers are used by those who farm on a large enough scale to justify mechanised feeding.

The best clamp silage is made from *leafy* plants (too much stem leads to overheating and spoiling, as well as being less nutritious) wilted down to 75 per cent moisture content within 24 hours of cutting (with an additive if necessary) and picked up in dry conditions, taking care not to pick up any soil from the field with the crop as that would encourage the less desirable butyric acid bacteria. Fill the silage store quickly, consolidate it and then seal it under an airtight cover. The exclusion of air from the heap is a very important factor in silage-making, whether the crop is grass, clover, lucerne, vetches, pea haulms, forage maize, whole-crop cereals, sugarbeet tops or anything else worth pickling. The other major factor is speed, and that means good equipment: you would be well advised to find a reliable contactor for the job. The stages are these, and appropriate equipment is described in detail in the Machinery section.

1. Cut the crop with a suitable mower, either straight into a trailer for carting or left on the ground to wilt. The machinery can either simply cut, or it can also 'condition' the crop by chopping or thrashing and tedding it, which hastens the early drying process. In ideal conditions, the standing-crop moisture levels of perhaps 80 per cent can be reduced by up to 10 per cent in 24 hours by wilting, or by 15 per cent in only six hours after conditioning. Additives can be used as inhibitors (to reduce clostridial activity and the amount of fermentation) or as stimulants (to encourage the production of lactic acid). Formic acid is a typical inhibitor; molasses or live lactobacilli are stimulants.

2. .Pick up the crop when it is ready and transport it in a forage-box or high-sided trailer to the silage store, or bag it.

3. Silage clamps or bunkers, above or below ground, need airtight walls (e.g. sleepers lined with plastic sheeting) and a concrete floor with carefully designed drainage so that the effluent does not become a pollutant. (It is rich in nutrients: save it and use as a feed.) Load the clamp with the help of a buckrake and fill the pit in wedges, as shown in the diagram. Cover each day's layer with plastic sheeting to keep air out until further loading takes place the next day. Consolidate as you load by running over the heap with the tractor wheels but take very great care to stay away from the edges, for safety's sake. When the heap is complete, and well consolidated, cover it finally and seal it, weighing down plastic sheeting with heavy tyres, strawbales, sand, soil, ground chalk, thick piles of wet grass or anything else heavy enough to hold it in place in all eventualities.

4. Bagging can be on a large or small scale: you could make very small quantities in thoroughly clean old fertiliser bags as long as they are absolutely sound and can be tightly sealed so that they remain airtight. Or you can invest in sausage-shaped black polythene silage bags, either filling them direct with carted silage or big-baling the silage and then wrapping the bales in the plastic. The main problems with bagging are the accumulation of effluent, the exclusion of air, and the possibility of damage to the containers by sharp items, rodents or strong winds.

Feeding silage

The problem of air exclusion continues when silage is fed and the aim is to expose as little surface area as possible. Either cut-and-carry by chopping out as much as you need for each feed, using a tractor with a fore or rear loader or grab or a screw block-cutter or one of the various vertical forklift accessories, carefully re-covering the surface before you take the feed to the animals, or let them help themselves at the silage face in

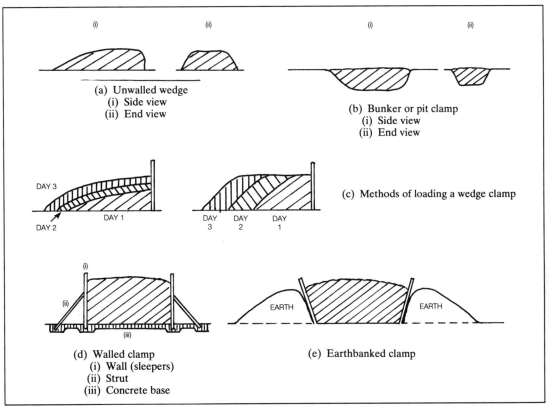

(a) Unwalled wedge
   (i) Side view
   (ii) End view

(b) Bunker or pit clamp
   (i) Side view
   (ii) End view

(c) Methods of loading a wedge clamp

(d) Walled clamp
   (i) Wall (sleepers)
   (ii) Strut
   (iii) Concrete base

(e) Earthbanked clamp

SILAGE CLAMPS

appropriate situations, designing the silage store accordingly. The maximum face height for cows is 2m, for calves 1.5m, for sheep 1m. If the face is too tall for the animals to reach, you will have to use a chainsaw or mechanical silage knife to slice the stuff off from the upper reaches and throw it down for feeding.

The width of exposed face depends on the number of animals requiring access at the same time: allow up to 25cm per cow, 17.5cm per beef animal, 10cm per calf, 10–12.5cm per sheep, if the animals have full-time access. You could reduce these allowances to two-thirds of the given widths, but you need to increase them if feeding time is limited.

The third dimension of your silage store — its length — is determined by how many animals you expect to feed and for how long a winter. In southern England the average is

150 days, increasing to perhaps 200 in northern England and so on.

Good silage smells more acid than sweet but even then does not smell much. It tastes sharp (try some!); it is clean to handle and is light green or light brown in colour. These are all signs that lactic acid is dominant, which means that the silage is very palatable to livestock, has a good feeding value and can last indefinitely as long as it is kept airtight conditions. If butyric acid bacteria have dominated the pickling process, the silage might still be reasonably nutritious but it will smell rancid and be not very palatable to the animals, nor will it keep for more than a few months; its colour will be khaki or olive green and its texture slimy rather than firm. If it is very butyric, it can even become toxic.

If oxygen finds its way in during the curing process, the silage overheats and its colour will be brown or black, the texture dry and the smell quite attractively sweet — somewhere between burnt sugar and tobacco. It is palatable but of low feeding value.

You cannot really tell the true quality of silage without having it professionally tested or by gauging its long-term effect on livestock production levels and you cannot really make best use of it as a feedstuff until you do know all there is to know about its feed value. Making good silage has many parallels with making good wine or good cheese: it is an art as well as a science and depends on quite a complicated combination of factors. Even those who specialise in silage production sometimes get it wrong, so don't be downhearted if your first attempts are less than successful.

II Fixtures

'The first step when a labourer intends to become a squatter is to enclose the strip of land which he has chosen. This he does by raising a low bank of earth round it, on which he plants elder bushes, as that shrub grows quickest, and in the course of two seasons will form a respectable fence. Then he makes a small sparred gate which he can fasten with a padlock, and the garden is complete.'

[Richard Jefferies,

The Toilers in the Field, 1892]

Boundaries

The establishment of good boundaries serves to fulfil psychological as well as practical needs. Boundaries define the extent of the property — the miniature kingdom, if you like — and good boundaries which have been carefully designed and created not only make for good neighbourly relationships but also give peace of mind, which is something definitely to be valued, especially if there are livestock on the holding.

External boundaries, defining the full extent of the property, can be of various kinds of fencing, or walls, or 'living fences' (hedges) but whatever their style, they must be permanent, soundly made and thoroughly stockproof, keeping out other people's stock even if you have none of your own to confine. It is always worth spending time and money on external boundaries: you can make savings on internal partitions but never skimp on your perimeters.

Check whether you or your neighbour is responsible for a mutual boundary and whether you can compromise to erect a barrier which suits both your purposes. In theory, it is the responsibility of the owner of livestock to control the animals, rather than up to others to fence them out, but in practice it would be wise to take precautions against possible invasions by wandering heifers in the early hours of Sunday morning (they have a wicked sense of timing).

Choices

There is a wide choice of materials, depending partly on the pocket, partly on practicalities such as availability of materials locally and the skill to use them, partly on the type of livestock, partly on personal preference and partly on regional customs. The latter should be taken into full account, not only because it is more aesthetic and visually acceptable to use locally traditional boundaries but also because there is probably very good reason for them being typical of the neighbourhood: they have proved themselves in that particular environment.

The Fencing Tables which follow set out the possible types of boundaries for different situations and suggest specifications for materials and heights. Bear in mind that hedges, although relatively slow to establish in comparison with the instant barrier of a fence, are excellent long-term investments: they increase in value year by year and will outlive you.

Fencing Tables

Strained Wire Fences (Plain or Barbed)
Barbed-wire (Cattle)

Straining	12–15cm×2.1–2.3m at 50–100m
Struts	10cm×2.1–2.4m
Stakes	10cm×1.7m at 2.7m
Wire	2 strands for adult cattle at 0.7/1.06m agl
	3rd strand for young cattle at 0.3m agl

Plain mild steel 4mm wire (Cattle, Sheep, Horses)

Straining	17.5cm×2.1m at up to 100m
Struts	7.5cm×2.1m
Stakes	7.5cm×1.7m at 2.7m
Wire	7 strands for cattle/horses at 7.5/17.5/30/ 45/75/95/106cm agl
	8 or more strands for sheep at 10cm intervals up to 0.5m, thereafter as cattle

Plain high-tension 3.15mm wire (Cattle, Sheep)

With wooden droppers:

Straining	Round 17.5cm×2.1m at up to 200m
Struts	10cm×2.1m
Stakes	7.5cm×1.7m at 10m
Droppers	3.8cm×2.6cm×1.1m at 2m
Wire	7 strands at 7.5/17.5/30/45/75/95/106cm agl

With steel droppers:

Strainers	Sawn 12.5cm×12.5cm×2.3m at up to 200m
Struts	Sawn 10cm×7.5cm×2.1m
Intermediates	Sawn 10cm×10cm×2m (7 drillholes) at 7.3m
Wire	7 strands at 10/22.5/37.5/55/75/100/ 124cm agl

Stock netting and wire mesh
Size/Suitability guides

Stock netting

	No. of line wires	Height (cm)	Dist. bet. verts. (cm)	Suitable for						
				C	S	L	G	P	H	D
Medium Weight Welded/Woven										
FF7 C8/11/30	8	115	30	C			G		H	
FF3 C6/90/30	6	90	30	C	S					
FF5 C8/80/30	8	80	30	C	S	L				
FF1 C8/80/15	8	80	15	C	S	L		P		
FF9	5	75	30		S	L				
Heavyweight Welded/Woven										
FF8	8	114.5	30	C			G		H	
FF4 B6/90/30	6	90	30	C	S				H	
FF6 B8/80/30	8	80	30	C	S	L				
FF2 B8/80/15	8	80	15	C	S	L		P		
High-Tensile Woven										
HT 13/190/15	13	190	15							D
HT 13/190/30	13	190	30							D
HT 8/90/30	8	90	30	C	S				H	
HT 8/90/15	8	90	15	C	S	L			H	
HT 8/80/30	8	80	30	C	S	L				
HT 8/80/15	8	80	15	C	S	L		P		

Hexagonal Mesh
Sheep Netting Sizes

Weight	Mesh size	Heights
14g	10cm	60cm, 90cm, 105cm
16g	7.5cm	90cm, 105cm
	10cm	45cm, 60cm, 75cm, 90cm, 105cm, 120cm
19g	7.5cm	60cm, 90cm, 120cm; 180cm

Hexagonal Wire Netting for other purposes

Poultry	19g, 38mm mesh
	19g or 17g, 50mm mesh
Rabbits	18g or 19g, 31mm mesh
Aviaries	19g or 22g, 13mm mesh
Vermin	22g or 20g, 19mm mesh

Stock Netting Specifications
Medium Weight C8/80/30 (Cattle, Horses, Sheep)

Straining	12.5cm×2.1m at up to 150m
Struts	10cm×2.1m
Stakes	6.3×1.7m at 2.7m
Netting	Base 5cm agl, top 85cm agl, stapled
Wires	3 extra lines 4mm mild steel at 3/95/ 105cm agl

Medium Weight lashed to Spring Steel Lines Wires (Cattle, Sheep)

Straining	15cm×2.3m at up to 200m
Struts	10cm×2.3m
Stakes	10cm×1.7m at 14m
Netting	Base 5cm agl, top 85cm agl, both lashed to 2.64mm spring steel support lines
Wires	1 extra wire 15cm above netting

Heavy Weight B8/80/15 (Cattle, Horses, Sheep, Lambs, Pigs)

Straining	17.5cm×2.1m at up to 150m
Struts	10cm×2.1m
Stakes	12.5cm×2.1m at 2.7m
Netting	Base 5cm agl, top 85cm agl, stapled
Wires	3 extra 4mm mild steel wires at 3/95/ 105cm agl

High-Tension HT 8/80/30 (Cattle, Horses, Sheep)

Straining	17.5cm×2.1m at up to 400m
Struts	10cm×2.1m
Stakes	7.5cm×1.7m at 8m
Netting	Base 10cm agl, top 90cm agl, stapled
Wires	2 extra 2.64mm spring steel wires at 5/105cm agl

Rabbit Netting (Hexagonal mesh) (Rabbits and livestock)

(The higher measurements are for spring steel wires, the lower with mild steel wires)

Straining	12.5cm×2.1–2.3m at 150–200m
Struts	10cm×2.1–2.3m
Stakes	6.3–7.5cm×1.7–1.8m at 10–15m
Netting	18g 31mm mesh, 1.05m high, top at 90cm agl, bottom 15cm buried and turned to lie horizontally against direction of rabbit attack. Ringed to support wires and stapled
Wires	4mm mild steel support wires at 5/45/90cm agl and 1 extra at 15cm above top of netting against livestock. OR: 2.64mm spring steel support wires at 5/50/90cm agl

Deer, with or without Livestock (Sheep, Goats) or Rabbits
Red, Sika and Fallow

Strainers	12–18cm×2.8m, buried 0.9m, up to 200m, or up to 400m with HT netting
Struts	12.5cm×2.5m
Stakes	8–10cm×2.5m at 10–14m
Netting	Top: FF3, FF5, C8/80/30, C6/90/30 or HT 8/80/30 Bottom: FF1, C8/80/15, C7/10/15 or HT 8/80/15 (plus 31mm 18g hexagonal for rabbits)
Wires	2.65mm spring steel at top, centre and base (5/95/185cm agl) for lashing to netting; extra line at 50cm for livestock

Roe deer, with or without Livestock/Rabbits

Straining	10–13cm×2.8m at up to 200m
Struts	8–10cm×2.5m
Stakes	5–8cm×2.5m at up to 14m
Netting	Top: Roe only: FF13 Roe/stock: FF13 or 19g 7.5cm hex. mesh×90cm Bottom: Roe only: FF13 Roe/stock: FF1, C7/10.15, C8/80/15
Wires	2.65mm spring steel at top, middle, base; additional wire halfway up lower section against livestock

Post-and-Rail
Riven Oak (Horses, Cattle)

Posts	7.5cm×12.5cm×1.8m, sunk 0.7m
Rails	30cm girth×2.8m, set at 20/55/92.5cm agl

Mortised Treated Softwood with Studs (Horses, Cattle, Sheep)

Posts	7.5cm×15cm×2m, sunk 0.8m
Studs	3.8cm×9cm×1.7m, at rail centres
Rails	3.8cm×9cm×2.9m, set at 34/69/105cm agl, or for sheep at 24/48/75/105cm, for lambs add 2 line wires (above and below bottom rail)

Nailed Sawn (Horses, Light Cattle, Sheep)

Posts	7.5cm×12.5cm×1.8m, sunk 0.7m
Rails	3.8cm×10cm×3.6m, set as for mortised softwood

Nailed Half-round (Horses, Light Cattle, Sheep)

Posts	10cm face (half-round)×1.8m, sunk 0.7m
Rails	7.5cm face×3.6m, set at 32.5/65/97.5cm agl

Electric Fencing
Temporary Cattle

Posts	Pigtails at 10m, tripods at corners, or poles (e.g. hazel) 5cm in diameter sunk 0.3–0.4m with nail-on insulators and split chestnut corner posts sunk 0.45m
Wire	Single line of polywire at 0.8–0.9m agl Add second lower wire for youngstock

Permanent Sheep/Cattle

Straining	15cm×2.1m at up to 200m
Stakes	3.8cm×3.8cm×1.5m at up to 40m
Droppers	3.8cm×2.6cm×0.9m at 10–20m
Wires	2.5mm HT — 3 for cattle, 5 for sheep at 15/29/47.5/67.5/90cm agl One could be scare wire, 2.64mm spring steel or 2.50mm mild steel, offset into field on brackets at 10–12m, at two-thirds the height of the animal

Temporary Sheep Netting

Plastic stakes are included with the netting. Height for sheep is 0.9m, for rabbits (smaller mesh) 0.5m, for trained goats 1.1m

Fieldguard Tape (most Livestock)

Consult distributors for details. Special stakes etc.

Horses	2 lines, top at 1.3m, lower at 70cm (60cm ponies); for temporary fencing, 1 line at 90cm
Cattle	1 line at 1.3m
Sheep	3 lines, top at minimum 75cm
Pigs	1 line

Site problems

Contours

It is easier, cheaper and usually visually more acceptable to erect your boundary on reasonably level ground, if you have a choice. Follow the contours to harmonise with the landscape but avoid marching a fence straight up a hill. Think of all your boundaries as an integral part of the landscape and take a long-distance view to imagine what effect they will have within it.

Slopes and uneven surfaces inevitably cause problems if livestock are to be contained by fencing: the animals are likely to find higher jumping-off points from slopes and embankments or, where the land dips, a ground-level gap through which they can shrug, squeeze or dig their way to freedom. Dips can also hold water, which will loosen and rot fencing posts when the water is standing or might act as a natural channel in times of flood so that the water current piles up debris against the fence. The combined weight of branches, leaves and water can flatten sheep-netting in no time and drag stakes right out of the ground. Treat such channel areas as ditches: there are ways of fencing across a ditch or gulley so that it is stockproof in dry times but allows a free flow in flood. (See Water gates.)

For simplicity's sake, as well as aesthetically, set fencing posts plumb vertical rather than at right angles to the surface of a slope, whether the fence is running up and down it or across it. On undulating ground, avoid being too rigid about the spacing of stakes: if you have a moderately artistic eye you will see that exaggerations in the fence line can be smoothed out by adjusting the spacings and post heights, especially with post-and-rail fences which, although they are better for fences which do not have a straight run, have a more obvious line in the landscape and draw attention to any aesthetic mistake. Hedges and walls, of course, flow more happily with the contours.

Soil

Take into account local variations in the soil. Obviously you will try to avoid driving stakes into difficult terrain littered with stones but bear in mind that the worst enemy of a stake, wall or hedge plant is a perpetually damp footing, especially within the frost layer. The damp rots the post and frozen soil expands (especially clay) so that the post is lifted during the winter and will need to be driven down again in spring. When frozen, soil and water expand by an eighth of their original volume: if the ground is frozen to a depth of, say, 8cm, the post will be lifted 1cm out of the lower unfrozen layer. Install some kind of drainage system along the fence-line in water-retaining soils such as peat or heavy clay by digging out a ditch and/or creating an embankment to make sure that water is taken away from at least the likely frost depth as well as from the surface.

Also watch out for areas subject to erosion, and try to avoid planting strain-bearing posts in shallow soil over rock. Bear in mind that in strong soils a post under pressure could snap, whereas in soft soils it is more likely to lean or lift out. Clay soils have the awkward habit of shrinking when they dry, and cracking wide open, which does little to maintain the stability of a post, whereas peaty soils and turves contain a lot of organic matter which will soon rot away, loosening the post.

Shape

To save on costs of material and labour, consider the most economical way of enclosing a given surface area, i.e. with the minimum practicable length of fence. For a start, the larger the area of the enclosure, the lower the fencing cost per square yard or metre: you can probably use much cheaper temporary fencing (e.g. electric) to divide up this large area, rather than investing considerable time and money on turning it into two or more permanent enclosures.

Naturally a straight run is cheaper than a curving or zigzagging line, and for most types of fencing it is also much easier to erect and more efficient. In the case of a strained wire fence, good long stretches of straight run are essential to the effectiveness of the fence.

The area enclosed by a given length of fencing is greatest as a circle but this is the most difficult to erect securely and is also likely to lose more than it gains in that there is an inevitable waste of space between adjoining circles. Forgetting hexagonals, the next least expensive enclosure (in terms of area enclosed for a given length of fencing) is a square: if you fence the same total land area within a long, thin rectangle, you will immediately need more posts, for a start. However, if a field is small and needs to be cultivated or harvested, a rectangle is more efficient than a square as it gives a longer working run with fewer headland turns.

Rationalise the shape: do not try to follow every innuendo of a naturally wavy outline but if the materials are suitable (e.g. post-and-rail) use smooth curves or, with post-and-wire fences, as long a straight run as possible between the main straining and corner posts unless this would be visually offensive. (There are no straight lines in a natural landscape!) If the boundaries are too complicated for simple straight runs, devise carefully planned zigzags with very wide angles. With wire fences you will need more substantial posts (straining posts, with struts to support them) at every change of direction, however slight, and also at awkward contour points such as in a dip or on a hump, and they are much more expensive and more laborious to set than intermediate stakes: keep them to a minimum by good design.

Stresses

Quite apart from the stress put on uprights by a strained wire fence, consider possible problems such as the weight of drifting snow or the force of the wind and take them into account when planning your choice of materials and designing the layout of the boundaries. Also think about animal behaviour: cattle and horses lean most of their weight on the top of a fence or hedge as they reach over for the greener goodies on the other side, and any post-supported fence should be built so that the wires or rails are on the livestock side of the posts: the posts themselves, rather than the staples or nails which attach the wire or rails to the posts, should take the animals' weight. Sheep prefer to push their way through a potential gap (which is why flexible netting can be so dangerous for them, especially lambs) whereas pigs either barge or try to root underneath. (The average outdoor pig farm on a commercial scale has about 20 miles of fencing!)

Preparation

Try to be methodical. Start by planning the fence-line, assessing where the major uprights need to be set (corner posts, straining posts, turning posts and so on) and watch out for

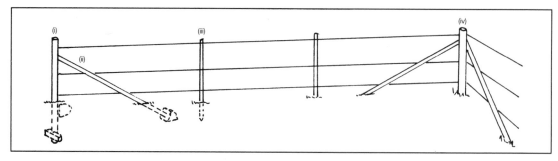

PARTS OF A WIRE FENCE

(i) End-of-run straining post   (ii) Strut   (iii) Intermediate stakes   (iv) Corner straining post

underground hazards such as cables and water-pipes. Try to time your fencing for ideal conditions: the soil needs to be soft enough for easy digging and post-driving but not so soft that vehicles leave ruts in pasture.

Your plans, especially for strained fences, should take into account the need to provide access points other than gates. All your good work in putting up a wire fence will soon be jeopardised if people climb over it and loosen the tension: put in a simple stile to keep human weight off the wire.

Uprights for fences

For a permanent fence, it is always worth investing money and labour to erect the major uprights which will support the whole structure, especially in a strained fence.

Fencing should be built to last, without the constant aggravation of frequent repairs. The uprights should be strong enough to take the weight of the fence in all conceivable circumstances: for example, livestock rubbing and pressing against it or trying to push through it, snowdrifts, floodwater debris and gales. However, it is wasteful to use materials of larger dimensions than necessary to withstand the likely stress: be guided by the Fencing Tables for appropriate measurements. The length of the posts depends on the type of livestock and also the texture of the soil but all posts need to be long-lasting in the ground and their longevity will be improved by good drainage at the footings, adequate post-hole depth, firm back-filling, the use of naturally durable or thoroughly

treated materials, and appropriate counteracting of the different strains to which the posts will be subjected. The terms used to describe different types of posts and their accessories are explained in the diagrams.

Never — but never — use a living tree as a fencing post. You run the risk of killing the tree in due course; you certainly ruin its potential value as timber, and as time goes by wire and fixings will be overgrown by bark and callus, making it impossible to remove them and leaving a dangerous, hidden obstruction for future chainsaws.

The choice of materials for uprights (whether to support rails, wire or netting) lies between concrete, metal, plastic, fibreglass and timber, which is the most common and versatile.

Concrete

It is not easy to make good enough concrete posts on the farm and it is better to buy reinforced precast ones. They should be set into concrete to a depth of 90cm if they are used as corner or straining posts and then given additional support with struts. They are not beautiful and are generally used with chainlink mesh, panel fencing or several lines of plain galvanised wire. For most stock, try seven wires set 12.5cm apart, the lowest at 10cm above ground level.

Angle-iron

These metal posts are only suitable for light fencing such as chainlink, rabbit wire or chicken wire, and perhaps for chestnut paling.

Plastic
In the true spirit of the green movement, posts are now being made from recycled plastic. They are self-insulating and therefore useful for electric fencing, or they can be used instead of timber posts (except that nailing and stapling might be a problem). Although still expensive at the moment, and hard to find, they are durable and require no maintenance.

Timber
Timber uprights are usually of sweet chestnut or pressure-treated softwood, or of oak if there is a ready source of supply or other locally available and naturally durable woods such as larch, yew and cedar. The naturally durable timbers (particularly oak and chestnut) are strongest in their heartwood, which is often darker than the outer layers of sapwood. This heartwood resists preservative treatments, but nor does it need them. A round post from a young stem of oak or chestnut will contain a much smaller proportion of heartwood than a stake split from a larger-diameter pole, but on the other hand sapwood can be permeated with preservative to protect it. Bark must be removed before poles are treated, though it is usually left intact on untreated chestnut poles.

Untreated oak posts should last for up to a quarter of a century in the ground, and untreated chestnut should last for at least 15 years on a well-drained site and perhaps more than twice as long in favourable circumstances. Most softwoods, however, must be treated with preservatives or they will soon rot. The old way is to steep them in creosote; today they are pressure-treated with substances such as copper sulphate and are described, according to the system used, as 'tanalised', 'celcurised' etc., claiming a life of perhaps 25 years if the treatment has penetrated thoroughly.

Cleft timber, split along its grain so that the fibres on the cleft face remain relatively intact and can shed rainwater, will last much better than sawn timber, in which the fibres have been damaged by the cutting. Chestnut posts are either round or are split in two (or more); oak is strongest when cleft but is also sometimes sawn for square posts. For post-and-rail fences, the uprights are either split or sawn so that they offer a flat face against the rails; the structure is strengthened by the rails themselves and it is not usually necessary to use struts against the posts. With strained wire fences, however, the wire exerts considerable tension on the end-of-run uprights and corner posts, which need to be very strong in themselves (round rather than split, and of large dimension and long enough for ample digging-in). They also need to be supported with angled struts against the direction of the strain, and relieved of some of the burden by substantial strutted straining posts set at intervals between the corners or end-of-runs.

The intermediate stakes between the straining posts merely serve to retain the line of the fence and only take the occasional pressure of leaning livestock. They are usually of round or split timber, set on the outside of the wire so that the staples (banged into the flat face if the post has been cleft) are not pushed out every time an animal pushes against the wire: the stakes, not the staples, take the strain.

Sawn posts for post-and-rail fences have 'weathered' tops; i.e. they are sawn at a slight angle to shed the rain.

To Set Posts
Always set posts deeper than you think is necessary: it will take more work initially but will make a stronger, longer lasting fence. It is particularly important to set really firm posts for strained wire fencing.

It is quicker to drive a post into undisturbed ground than to dig a hole for it; and a driven post will be the more secure. A machine-driven post is even firmer than a hand-driven one. However, large straining posts need to be dug in and then thoroughly tamped and strutted so that they hold firm. Always use larger, longer posts if the anchorage is jeopardised by disturbed ground or if they have to be set into 'weak' soils like peat, soft clay or fine silt.

Hand-driven posts

Hand-driving is suitable for intermediate stakes along a strained wire fence if you do not have access to a tractor-mounted post-driver.

Point the stake but blunt the tip to prevent it snapping off. Start the post hole with something like a crowbar or an old buckrake tine: ram it in vertically and stir it about a little, but try not to open the hole too wide at the surface as you need a really snug fit for the post at ground level. Use a wooden maul or beetle or a rubber or cast-iron mell to bang the post down, taking care not to split its top. The broad face of a mell spreads the force of the blow but the smaller face of a metal sledge-hammer could massacre the post. Do not ask some innocent bystander to hand-hold the post while you attempt to drive it in; rather than risk a smashed hand from a mistimed hit, the assistant should use a post-holder.

Aim to have about a third of an intermediate stake in the ground and drive it in absolutely vertical from all points of view. One problem might be that the stake, before being driven, stands too high for you to hit it strongly and squarely: you will either need to stand on, say, a trailer or to make the starting hole large enough to swallow more of the stake when you drop it into position.

There are various devices, homemade or otherwise, to help with this hard work but some are more of a fiddle than they are worth. The basic post-driver is the Drivall type, which is a capped heavy metal pipe with handles on each side: the cap fits over the top of the post and is slightly lifted by its handles (by one person or two) and then dropped so that its own weight drives the post into the ground. This takes practice and a reasonable amount of strength: the action will probably send vibrations through your body and ring loud in your ears, but skilled users find it less hard work than driving with a mall or beetle and it is less likely to split the top of post. The inexperienced should beware of rasping their knuckles against the guide wire set up for aligning the stakes.

Tractor-mounted post-drivers

If a tractor and attachments are available, this is certainly the quickest, least tiring and most efficient method of post-driving, whatever the size of the post. The possible drawback is making a mess of the land if the season is wet but at least the tractor doubles up as a transporter for the posts. You can also attach an auger for drilling post-holes.

Dug posts

You will need a spade, of course, or a hand-held manual or power-driven post-hole auger or, if you are dealing with bedrock, a rock drill, pickaxe and crowbar. There is a considerable choice of spades, according to the type of ground, but a rabbiting spade is probably the most useful (and some are designed so that the handle can be used as a soil rammer). More sophisticated are scoop-shovels or gadgets like the Shuv-holer which are basically two narrow-bladed, pointed spades hinged together like tongs so that loosened soil can be removed as you dig. It is very difficult to scoop out soil with an ordinary spade at more than a spade's depth.

You also need something to tamp the soil around the post — preferably something better than the heel of your boot. You could improvise with a crowbar, a sledge hammer or a hefty chunk of hardwood.

Undisturbed soil makes the most secure surroundings for any post and you should aim to dig as narrow a hole as possible (hence the rabbiting spade). The best compromise is to dig a vertical-sided hole in which the post will stand off-centred, hard against an undisturbed face for the greatest support against the direction of the greatest strain on the post. If it is a strainer post for a wire fence (especially in soft soil) give it greater stability by attaching a short crossbar at its foot, digging the hole to accept the shape. The crossbar is a piece of half-round (split) pole about half a metre long, nailed into a notch near the foot of the post on the opposite side to the line of pull. Wedge this with a heavy stone before backfilling the hole and then give the post a stone breastblock just below ground level. On a wet site, a second crossbar could be fixed further up the underground section of the post. In some conditions it is necessary to set straining posts in concrete.

Note that for mortised post-and-rail fencing the post-hole needs to be dug wide enough to allow the post to be tilted as it is negotiated to fit its rails. Sawn posts, or even round or split ones where looks are important, will have to be dug in rather than driven to avoid damaging their tops.

Mechanical post-hole augers or borers have corkscrew-like cutters and are driven by their own small petrol engines (like chainsaws are). They can be quite dangerous in careless hands. Choose the correct type of auger for the ground: a plain cutter with a fishtail tip in soft ground, or a serrated cutter with a tungsten tip if the site is hard. Start the engine according to the manufacturer's instructions. Keep your back straight and lift the implement by using your leg and arm muscles, standing firmly with your feet well clear of the machine's tip. Lower it slowly — you do not want to strike hard ground suddenly. Use it like an enlarged do-it-yourself drill: let the machine do the work and do not exert undue pressure but maintain an auger speed and drilling pressure appropriate to the conditions. Let it continue to rotate as you remove it from the bored hole.

Backfilling

Backfill a post-hole gradually, tamping each layer thoroughly as you do so, especially in the deepest regions. If necessary, use a crowbar to ram in some small stones or aggregate for extra strength. Backfill proud: leave a slight mound of soil surrounding the post to shed water away from it so that rotting at ground level is avoided.

Struts

For wire fences, straining posts (and also turners where the angle of change of direction is more than about 30 degrees) need the further support of struts. The diagrams suggest various methods of strutting but the most common is a long, round pole set at an angle and wedged into a birdsmouth notch or mortise at a point on the strainer about

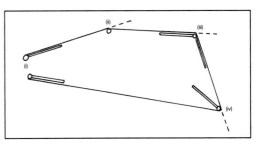

THE NEED FOR STRUTS
(i) End posts
(ii) Turning post: angle less than 30 degrees
(iii) Corner post: angle more than 30 degrees
(iv) Acute corner: angle more than 90 degrees

two-thirds to three-quarters of the height of the fence's top wire, forming an angle of about 30 degrees. The foot of the strut is buried well into the ground, pressing against a thrust plate of some kind if the soil is not stable. The strut's bed is a rabbit-scrape of a hole, with a vertical face of undisturbed soil to prop its butt, reinforced with a good strong stone against the face as a thrust plate. Alternatively, forget about digging

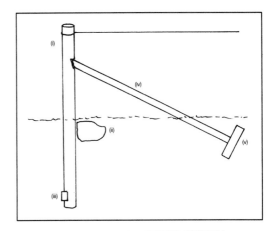

PARTS OF A STRUTTING SYSTEM
(i) Straining post
(ii) Breast block
(iii) Foot
(iv) Strut
(v) Thrust plate or bed plate

out rabbit-scrapes and set the foot of the strut at ground level, using half a stake (round or split) as a thrust plate, pointed so that it can be driven into the ground at an

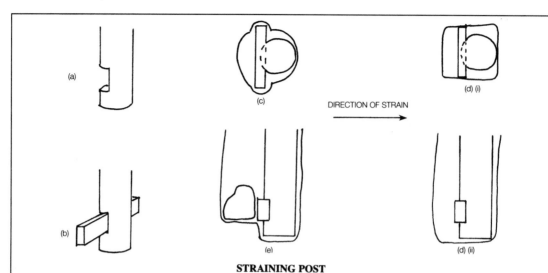

DIRECTION OF STRAIN

STRAINING POST

The post is set against the undisturbed face of the hole

(a) Notch for foot
(b) Foot in place (sawn or half-round timber)
(c) Post-hole shaped for foot

(d) Simple post-hole
  (i) From above
  (ii) From side

(e) Stepped post-hole to take the extra support of a heel stone in soft ground

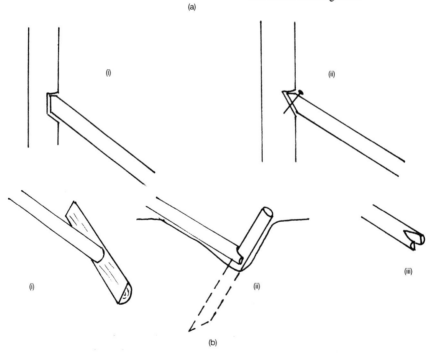

STRUT FIXTURES

(a) Straining-post notches for top of strut
  (i) Mortised
  (ii) Birdmouth

(b) Wooden stobs as thrust plates at base of strut
  (i) Horizontal half-round stob
  (ii) Vertical round stob
  (iii) Strut notch for round stob

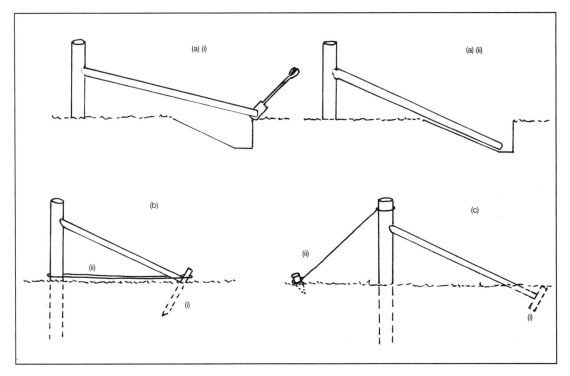

SETTING A STRUT

(a) Rabbit-scrape hole
   (i) Strut ready to be levered into place
   (ii) Strut in position, before hole is backfilled

(c) Strut partially sank
   (i) Timber stob as thrust plate
   (ii) Wire guy to short anchor stake

(b) Strut not sunk
   (i) Base nailed to round or half-round timber stob driven into ground
   (ii) Retaining wire around base of post and top of stob for extra support

angle and at right angles to the strut. The strut is nailed to the thrust plate and to the straining post. The strength of the structure lies in the third side of the triangle: a retaining wire of spring steel just above the ground is looped around the base of the post and the projection of the thrust plate and is then tightened and stapled. The diagrams show the various parts of strutting systems.

Struts should not be fixed until at least two straining posts have been set. Then run a strained bottom wire as a guide line so that the struts can be aligned as closely as possible to the direction of the strain but without interfering with the wire. You can either fit the top of the strut into the strainer's notch first and then lever its foot into place against the thrust plate with a spade, or put the foot in place first and then tap the top end into its wedge. It must finally be so firmly wedged between strainer and thrust plate that it is almost impossible to shift it in any direction. Then you can backfill the hole.

Another common system is the box strainer, seen more often in America and Australasia than Britain. You need two uprights, driven into the ground rather than dug, and braced by a horizontal bar bolted into notches near the top of each post. A diagonal wire is run from the top of one post to loop round the other at just above ground level and back again so that it forms a double run, and then the wires can be tightened with a simple windlass: a piece of timber is used as a lever to twist them together so that the wires will

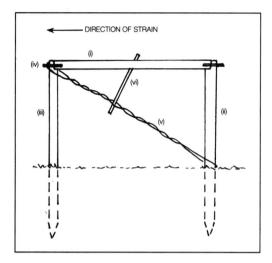

BOX STRAINER
(i) Rail 2.3cm × 10cm
(ii) Post 2.2m × 12.5cm
(iii) Post 2.2m × 10cm
(iv) Steel bar driven in to secure post and rail, and left protruding to anchor retaining wire
(v) Retaining wire, double strand, twisted together
(vi) Twitch stick (windlass) to tighten wires by twisting

take the fence's strain. A similar method is used to form a box strut for corner posts or turners.

Repairs
To save the major operation of rebuilding a fence when a strainer or rail post has rotted at or below ground level, set a short second post beside it (dig or drive as appropriate) and bolt or nail the two together.

Dips and soft spots
To deter stock from crawling to freedom if the ground dips here and there along the fence line, either bridge the dip with rails and extra wires or fill it in with rubble to raise it to adjacent levels, or site a straining post in the dip to take the fence line down into it if appropriate, or use an intermediate stake firmly pegged down so that it is not lifted out of the ground by the strain of the wire. Use a windlass system to counteract the strain on the tent-peg principle: drive in two stakes at angles on either side of the post, ramming them right into the ground so

that only a stub protrudes; wire the post to these peg-stakes by stapling a wire end to the peg, running it round the stake and back to the peg again for stapling, and repeating the procedure with the second peg. Then put a bar of metal or strong wood between the two parallel wires and twist it like a tourniquet until the wires are taut; remove the bar and do the same for the second peg. Or make a proper box strainer, described above.

A tip from the past: for any fence, set the posts and then throw up an earth embankment along the run at least 6–10in high, with a smooth, level centre. As well as shedding

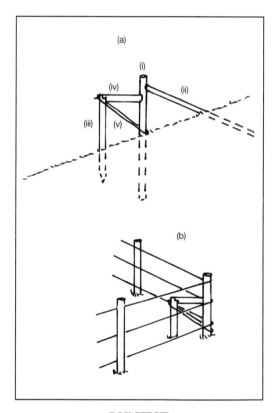

BOX STRUT
(a) On a slope
  (i) Main post
  (ii) Strut
  (iii) Short post
  (iv) Rail, secured to short post by steel bar
  (v) Retaining wire, double strand
(b) Supporting a corner post

water into the ditch created by making the embankment, it fills any escape-route dips and gives the posts extra footing.

Wire fencing

Wire fencing includes those with several strands of plain steel wire stretched horizontally, or fewer strands of barbed wire, or various kinds of wire netting, either flexible or rigid. It also includes electrified fences. The factors involved include the thickness of the wire: the higher its gauge number, the thinner the wire, but not necessarily the weaker. Tensile strength (which reflects the maximum load on a wire before it snaps under tension) is related not only to the diameter of the wire but also to its constituents and method of manufacture, which govern its elasticity. Diameter plays its part: thinner wires return more readily to their original length when they have been stretched. Thin wire is lighter and cheaper but is not as strong as thicker ones of the same type.

All fencing wire should be galvanised (i.e. zinc-coated) to reduce corrosion of the steel. Galvanising can be damaged by atmospheric pollution (particularly salt-laden coastal air or industrial sulphur dioxide), mechanical abrasion (for example, rubbing against loose-fitting staples, or kinked by tight stapling and careless use of tools) and contact with certain chemicals.

Mild steel wire has been used for many years in post-and-wire fencing. Its drawback, in comparison with some other types of wire, is that it responds readily to temperature changes, stretching and slackening when it is warm and in due course failing to retain its ability to spring back to its original length, so that it needs supporting at frequent intervals to retain its effectiveness as a livestock barrier. Stakes should be 3–5 m apart, which means a considerable input of materials and labour when the fence is erected.

Spring steel wire costs much the same as mild steel wire and weighs less but is much more stable. In spite of its smaller gauge, its breaking point is higher and it retains its tension so that you need far fewer straining posts and stakes. Strainers could be as far apart as a thousand metres in ideal situations (though 200 m is more common) and stakes 14 m apart, so that you will save on the cost of posts. However, you will need special tools because it is less easy to handle and is more susceptible to damage if tools are inappropriate. For example, any bends must be U-shaped, not V-shaped, in order to avoid weakening the wire; it is too hard to be cut with pliers (you need a hacksaw or wire-cutters); it kinks as it is unwound from the reel unless you use a wire-dispenser.

As a simple post-and-wire fence, spring steel wire can be effective against quiet sheep but it is not infallible with deer or cattle and is best used to support stock netting.

High tensile wire is used in some types of agricultural fencing. It is more elastic than mild steel wire and maintains tension in warm weather or under impact but it does have a tendency to brittleness and can snap at weak points if it is overstrained, which could cause injuries. Indeed the Forestry Commission would not recommend its use, preferring spring steel wire. HT wire is perhaps best used in electric fencing, where it does not need to be so tightly strained.

Barbed-wire has been the cattle farmer's favourite for more than a century but it is barbarous stuff and should not be used if there are alternatives. It injures people and animals (domesticated or wild); it lurks dangerously in the undergrowth or works its way relentlessly into the bark of living trees; it damages potentially useful hides, it lacerates the more tender skin of horses and wild deer (have you heard the heart-rending scream of a young deer meeting barbed-wire for the first time in its life as it flees?), it gets entangled with fleeces, it infuriates ramblers, and any cow worth her bull can jump a fence and could end up with an irreparably scored udder. It can also be lethal, and should never be used where wild deer are known to be present. Barbed-wire is a stopgap, used where hedge or wall maintenance has been neglected or where kinder and equally effective materials have not been considered. There are alternatives and they should be considered — barbed-wire should be used only as a last resort and it is the sign of a bad farmer taking a cheap shortcut. But it is undeniably useful!

Most people use mild steel barbed-wire though there is also high tensile wire; and in both cases it is important to use two-ply types. Single-ply barbed wire is cheaper but a poor investment: it will not last long in mild steel and in high tension wire it is awkward to handle and brittle enough to snap as you tension it — very dangerous.

Electric wire is now often a combination of thin plastic or polypropylene braid interwoven with current-conducting wire filaments and there are several types on the market. The old type was lightweight galvanised mild steel of various gauges, either quite plain or of several strands twisted together: it was rather heavy and awkward to handle and could get in a terrible tangle. The plastic-and-filament types are much lighter, cleaner and cheaper, they are easier to reel,

cut and join and do not coil themselves wilfully into inextricable loops as soon as you let go. They are also more visible, which is of benefit in training stock to respect the fence and acts as a warning to human beings as well. However, they are not such good conductors as pure wire and are only used for temporary fences in runs of up to perhaps 600m. For permanent electric fencing, use HT wire or HT wire netting.

The newest idea is an electrified webbing tape incorporating metal filaments: it is highly visible and particularly useful for containing horses for that reason, but it is also now widely used (in Scandinavia in particular) for outdoor pig systems and other livestock. Note that line wire fences, electrified or not, are almost as disastrous for horses as barbed-wire: the animals career, flee, panic and blunder into the wire they fail to see. High tension wire is aptly dubbed 'cheese-cutter' by horse keepers.

Strutted corner-post for hexagonal sheep-netting, with a hawthorn hedge as protection from Norfolk winds. *(Anna Oakford).*

Wire netting has become very popular in the last two decades, since the introduction of spring steel wire and, more recently, new techniques in netting manufacture. The traditional type is of *hexagonal* mild-steel mesh (chicken wire, rabbit netting, sheep netting) which is lightweight, easy to handle and versatile but only strong enough to confine or exclude smaller animals. It is often used in combination with stock netting or field fencing to keep browsers away from plantations and is still used for temporary sheep netting, which has a three-ply selvedge along top and bottom for greater rigidity and an additional central strand running horizontally the full length of the roll.

Hexagonal netting is far from rigid in itself: the wires are twisted together at their point of contact in a horizontal plane and the netting is easily pulled out of shape. However, it is cheap and it can be temporarily stapled straight to the stakes or can be attached to strained top and bottom line wires (mild steel or HT) by rings or ties to give it more strength.

A second type of woven netting in high tensile or mild steel is now made using horizontal and vertical wires in a *hinge-joint* system to give oblong or square mesh patterns. It retains a degree of flexibility, especially in a vertical plane, which might be useful if the fence-line is along uneven terrain but is otherwise undesirable (it can concertina). This problem is overcome by using *welded* mesh, a simple network of horizontal and vertical wires welded together where they meet. Welded mesh is of mild steel; high tensile steel cannot be welded. Although most people simply staple the netting (known as field fencing) to stakes for sheep-netting, in fact both woven and welded types are designed to be strained, which makes for a more effective and tidier fence altogether. If the netting is lashed to supporting lines of strained spring steel or HT wire, far fewer stakes will be needed and the costs and labour of erecting the fence are considerably reduced.

These woven or welded grid-pattern types of stock netting are available in various weights, widths and mesh sizes for different

Hinge-jointed pig-netting. The base-board deters young animals from rooting under the fence. *(Anna Oakford).*

applications and are coded accordingly. For hinged-joint netting, the coding system uses a letter to indicate the grade, based on the diameter and tensile strength of the wire (L = Light, C = Medium, B = Heavy, HT = High Tensile) followed by the number of horizontal wires; the second number gives the fence height and a final number gives the spacing between the vertical wires (both in centimetres). For example, C8/80/15 is a typical all-purpose stock fence of medium grade suitable for cattle and sheep: it has eight horizontal wires, a total height of 80 cm, and vertical wires 15 cm apart. Welded fencing has a different coding system: the equivalent of the example given would be FF1 with BRC's 'Weldfence'.

In general the horizontal wires are designed to be closer together towards the bottom of the fence: make sure you set it the right way up! This is particularly important with smaller animals or youngstock: if the mesh size is too large they run the risk of jamming their heads through it and soon loosen the fence in their attempts to struggle free. However, should you for some reason want chickens or pheasants to have free access through the fence (and they will not fly over unless in a panic, though they might spend a long time trying to squeeze through) set the fence upside down if the closer-set lower mesh is too small for them.

Please do *not* use polythene or nylon netting for stock. Animals can easily become entangled in it and almost garotte themselves, especially wildlife, sheep and lambs — and horses can literally pull off a hoof in their panic. If you use electric sheep netting (polythene with wire filaments) make sure that it is *always* electrified, but even then wild animals such as deer, not trained to the fence, can get into severe difficulties.

Products such as chain-link or Twilweld do not have many agricultural fencing applications. Both are used as security fencing, especially in urban areas; Twilweld is also used to make animal pens or fruit cages and, in heavier grades, for hay racks, sheep pens, gates and dividers.

Setting up a wire fence

The order of work is: dig in your main posts, then run a bottom line of wire first, as a guide for the fence-line, straining it to get a dead straight run between the straining posts. Put the struts against their strainers without interrupting the fence-line. Now run the top wire and strain it; then align intermediate stakes, guided by the wires, with each stake plumb vertical and *just* touching the wires, then bang in the stakes. Strain and attach remaining wires or netting, and finally fill in any potential escape routes formed by the unevenness of the terrain, using extra wires, rails or netting, or filling in firmly with rocks or sods.

Barbed-wire

For a cattle-proof barbed-wire fence you will need round *straining posts* at approximately 50m intervals (with end-posts, corner posts and turning posts where appropriate), struts to strengthen each straining post (one or two according to the circumstances), split or round intermediate stakes at every three strides between the straining posts, and at least two lines of galvanised two-ply barbed-wire for quiet adult cattle, or three for more active animals and youngstock. You also need galvanised staples, a hammer and wire-cutter, a wire-strainer, and equipment for setting the posts. Work in the following order:

First erect all the straining posts, set 0.9m deep and very firmly backfilled. Before fixing the struts, run a temporarily strained bottom wire as a guideline for them and cut strut notches into the straining posts, aligned. along (and against) the direction of strain. Now you can dig in the struts and wedge them into their notches.

Next, fix and strain the top wire as a guide for the intermediate stakes. Mark the position of the stakes in a dead straight line between the straining posts, making sure that they will be on the outside of the wire so that the stakes, not the staples, will take the pressure of livestock leaning on the fence.

If the ground is not reasonably level, drive in the stakes which come at high or low points along the line first (to give height lines) and then the rest, starting with halfway stakes to keep the line true. Ensure that all the stakes are vertical in all planes and that they do not distort the straight run of the wire between the straining posts: their faces (preferably split-side) should *just* touch the wires.

Staple the top wire to the stakes, adjust its tension finally and fasten off at the end of the run. Set, strain and staple any other lines required. As a finishing touch, trim off the stake tops to about 5cm above the top wire for a level look and give the tops a coating of preservative if necessary.

Handling barbed-wire
One of the reasons that barbed-wire has rapidly lost ground to other forms of fencing is that handlers find it vicious, heavy and awkward. Always wear very strong gloves to reduce the possibility of injury when handling barbed-wire. Keep it carefully rolled: if you are dealing with old wire, roll it up round a stake as you dismantle it, and for new wire

unwind it from the reel as you go by slipping a sturdy rod through the reel, preferably with one person holding one end of the rod and a second the other. Keep it taut and free-running and dispense it without jerky movements. Watch out for its unpleasant habit of coiling rapidly back on itself given the chance, and *never* stand on or astride the wire while it is being tensioned!

Straining barbed-wire

This can be very dangerous work for the inexperienced. The aim is to strain the wire as tightly as you dare (a slack wire is no deterrent to livestock) but not so much that it suddenly snaps and whiplashes across the field, which could cause very serious injuries if anyone happens to be in its unpredictable path. Practise by straining plain wire before tackling barbed-wire. Invest in a tension gauge if you cannot trust your judgement.

Start by fixing the beginning of the wire firmly to the first straining post, taking a couple of turns around the post and stapling the wire to it to make quite sure it cannot spring free when it is being strained. Unwind from the reel as already described until you reach the second straining post.

The most common *wire-straining tool* is the monkey, a length of chain with various types of grips at either end and a lever or ratchet system. Loop one end of the chain around the straining post and secure it by its grip-hook so that it is just clear of the horizontal line of the wire itself, with the loose length on the stock side of the post. Checking that the chain links are not twisted, attach the grip on the free end to the wire at a point which pulls the wire fairly taut even before you start ratcheting. Now work the lever system, link by link, until it is as strained as required (usually when any further leverage becomes difficult). A short length of wire will remain on the post side of the wire-strainer at this point: use a claw hammer to work it around the post and then fix it with staples.

It is possible, with skill, to use a claw hammer instead of a wire-strainer for barbed-wire. Set the wire in position, pulling it reasonably tight by hand, and hold it to the post with a staple loose enough to let the wire run through it quite easily but tight enough to retain it against a barb. Use the hammer as a pivot, resting its head against the post and catching a barb in the claw, then gradually levering the wire round the post, barb by barb, until it is adequately strained so that it can be firmly stapled.

Some people use a tractor to strain wire but this can be very dangerous indeed: the risk of whiplash is that much greater.

Stapling

The main rules with staples are:

Use a size and weight appropriate to the task.

Do not drive a staple into a post in a vertical alignment: it will probably split the wood along its grain. Set each staple at a slight angle, and also avoid lining up two staples along the same grain: offset them slightly from each other.

On intermediate stakes, where the role of the staple is more as a method of keeping the wire horizontal than taking its linear strain, the staple should just touch the wire. Do not drive it home as it will tend to distort and thus weaken the wire, and will damage the galvanising. It will also put a greater strain on the point of contact whenever an animal leans on the wire: the aim should be to spread this type of pressure along the whole length of the wire by stapling to a 'running fit'. In any case, the wire needs to be able to 'breathe' in the staple's grip as it expands and contracts with changes of temperature. Remember, too, that one day you will no doubt want to remove the staple without having to resort to a hacksaw. However, if the staple is too loose the wire will be shaken by the wind and its galvanising will gradually be eroded so that, again, the wire will weaken at that point.

Here is a little tip, originally suggested during the 19th century when barbed-wire was a considerable hazard to the local hunt. If you want to staple a wire in such a way that you can remove it easily without removing the staple, drive two staples horizontally into the post, immediately above and below the wire line, and keep the wire in place between them by dropping a galvanised slate-nail (which has a large flat head) through the two staples so that it hangs by its head from the top staple. Then simply take out the nail to release the wire when necessary.

If the wire changes direction slightly (for example, at a turning point in the fence or at a high or low point), put two running-fit staples side by side and a little apart to avoid kinking the wire at a single pressure point.

On straining posts, staples take some of the wire's strain and need to secure it firmly rather than let it run. Angle the staple's points nearer to the horizontal than the vertical and drive it in so that the staple pinches the wire but does not kink it. However, do not rely solely on the staple to secure the wire: it is likely that in due course the weathering of the post will loosen the staple. It is safer to take at least two turns of the wire round the post anyway and then twist its end over itself as well as stapling.

Plain wire

Very similar methods can be used for straining plain wire. It is much easier to handle than barbed-wire, but bear in mind that spring steel wire is as eager to recoil and can cause injuries. To avoid this, and to avoid the inevitable kinking if you unroll by hand, use a wire dispenser. The dispenser also makes the whole job less tiring and quicker: you don't carry the reel with you as you unwind it but deposit the dispenser flat on the ground, or in a vehicle travelling along the line. Either buy a metal one, which has arms to keep the coil intact, or devise one from a timber cross base pivoted to a swivel stump in the ground, with large bent nails to retain the coil. Put the wire in the dispenser in such a way that its starting end is at the bottom of the coil. Watch out for the sharpness of a wire's loose ends, which can spike your hands.

Plain wires can be strained with a monkey strainer but make sure that the tool is suitable if you are using spring steel wire, which is easily damaged by the strainer's grips.

Avoid bending mild steel wire back on itself when stapling it to a straining post: you will damage the galvanising. Instead, let it curve in U-bends, perhaps snaking it in an S-shape on the post. Do not use straining-post staples to finish off spring steel or HT wire, however: instead, knot and twist the loose end over the main run of the wire if it is HT (the same system can be used for mild steel), or use radisseurs, ratchet winders, preformed fence connectors or lashing rods. With ratchets, make sure that the wire is given two full turns on the ratchet before the strainers are released, and with any straining system secure the wire on either side of the cutting point before actually cutting the wire.

Joining wires

To mend a broken wire, use a wire-strainer to draw the two ends together and then join them by knotting or using a connector or lashing rod. If this would overstrain the wires, insert an additional length of new wire between them. Connectors are preferable to knots, as the system is bound to be weakened where the pieces rub against each other in the knot and are kinked. Most vulnerable of all is the simple loop-and-twist, when all the strain is taken at the weak point where the wire loops meet.

Similar methods can be used to connect wire from a new reel when the old one runs out, but it would be preferable to site your posts so that mid-run joins are avoided.

Preformed *fence connectors* and *lashing rods* are particularly suitable for spring steel wires. Both are basically spirals of wire which are wrapped around the two pieces of wire to be joined: the grip of the spiral will increase as it elongates, rather like those childhood trick fingerstalls with a diagonal weave that become tighter the harder you tried to pull them off. Connectors are of three strands of wire and are used for joining or terminating spring steel wires or HT woven wire netting; lashing rods are single strands and are used mainly to attach woven or welded netting to spring steel line wires.

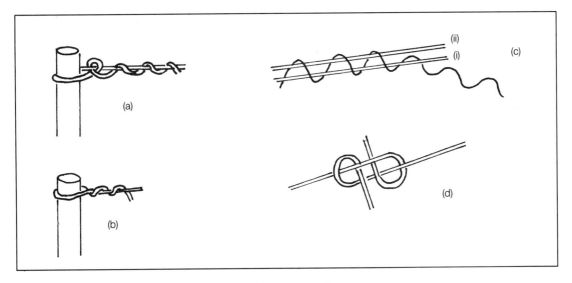

JOINING WIRES

(a) Knot system for finishing off mild steel or HT wire
(b) Twisting system for finishing off mild steel wire
(c) Lashing rod connecting (i) top of netting to (ii) top of line-wire
(d) Double-six or figure-of-eight knot for joining mild steel or HT wire

Lashing rods should only be used with welded or woven netting, choosing an appropriate size for the grade of fencing. Their name is descriptive: they lash the line wire and the top or bottom horizontal of the netting together. A short length of wire makes a useful lever for winding the spiral on to the wires.

To use a connector to fix the end of a wire run at a straining post, loop the wire round the post and use a loose staple to hold it at the right height, with a tail of at least 50 cm of wire, round the end of which half the connector is wrapped (there is a paint mark on the connector showing its centre point). Now wrap the other half around the main run of the wire. If the wire is under strain, keep the strainer in place until the connector has been clicked into place. To join two loose ends, use two connectors: starting at the paint mark, wrap one half of one of them around the first wire, then the other half around the second; now do exactly the same with the second connector, winding it along the spaces between the spirals of the first.

Droppers

Droppers are lightweight posts which rest on the ground rather than being dug in: their role is to keep wires evenly spaced and deter livestock from pushing between them. Wire spacers do the same job in mid-air and are usually of light metal.

Although HT wire is by its nature exceptionally strong and the need for intermediate stakes is greatly reduced, the wires do need to be kept equidistant along its length. The droppers can be of galvanised steel (in length half the total distance between the top and bottom wires) which are set staggered along the line at intervals (one to the top wire, the next to the bottom wire) and are attached with clips, or they can be of cleft chestnut pales or pressure-treated wooden battens running from the top wire to the bottom wire (or the ground) and attached by running staples set at alternate angles to each other to keep the batten in place. These battens, long enough to span from top wire to bottom and measuring perhaps 50 × 38 mm, are evenly spaced between the stakes. (To drive in the staples, put the head of a heavy hammer behind them as you drive.) Set the staples at alternate angles for each wire so that the wires do not slip sideways. A third type is the HT steel dropper, manufactured in a twisting design to be woven among the wires.

If you want to draw the line of a wire fence down slightly towards a dip, use a drilled tie-down stake. Drive the stake almost full-length into the ground, at an angle like a tent peg, then thread a wire through a hole at the top of the stake and bind it round the lower end of a dropper in the fence. Alternatively, tie the base of the dropper to something heavy like a rock or log, which is rested in the dip and then buried.

Wire netting

Standard field netting requires stakes about three paces apart between straining posts which can be up to 150m apart; HT netting, which is much stronger in itself, requires fewer stakes but more robust straining posts.

Straining netting

Stock netting should be erected with the widest spacings at the top and should be properly strained for best results. Follow the same procedure as for setting up any other strained wire fence. If you have only one straining tool, use it for the bottom of the fence first, but you would do better with two tools so that you can deal with top and bottom at the same time, and better still with straining boards for really even tension throughout the height of the fence. Ready-made boards incorporate their own straining devices, or you can adapt your own system by using simple boards with hooks to take an ordinary strainer's grip. Or, even more simply, wrap the end of the netting around a strong, rigid iron bar as long as the height of the roll.

Straining boards are used in pairs, with the end of the roll of netting clamped between them, thus held rigid so that the force of the straining is spread over the whole width of the fencing.

For a stronger fence, stretch a plain line wire (preferably of spring steel) immediately above the top of the netting, to which it should be joined with lashing rods. Then the netting itself need only be lightly strained — and it is much easier to strain lines than netting. It is really the only way to make a good fence of hexagonal mesh, and is also the preferred method with woven or welded netting. Alternatively, forget about straining wire or netting and instead use half-round wooden top rails face down above the netting to make the whole structure rigid by nailing them to posts — but of course this will mean extra expenditure on materials. A strained line of plain wire at the base of the fence will help to keep it firm against nudgers.

Sheep not only push their heads through netting (and frequently get stuck by the ears) but also walk up it with their forefeet to reach tempting titbits on the other side, gradually slackening the fence, while pigs tend to root underneath the netting, and goats — well, goats are goats. Many stock fences have at least two strained plain wires above the netting, partly to give it extra height but mainly to take the strain of a leaning animal and thus avoid pressure on the netting. A run of poles or boards, or the addition of hexagonal mesh above the main fence might also help to give extra height against leaping goats and mountain sheep, while for deer and possibly for goats it is common practice to have a two-tier woven or welded netting fence supported by spring steel line wires (at least three) and with full-height intermediate stakes up to 14m apart. Whether the fence is normal stock height or two-tier, do not be tempted to use barbed-wire as a top line because of the damage it can cause to a jumping animal.

The usual order of work for stock netting is as follows. Set at least two straining or end posts and also any intervening turning or contour posts, then set and tension bottom and centre wires (if used). Space the intermediate stakes, guided by the wires, and drive them in. Staple the bottom wire to the stakes, then run, tension and likewise staple any other wires, starting with the lowest.

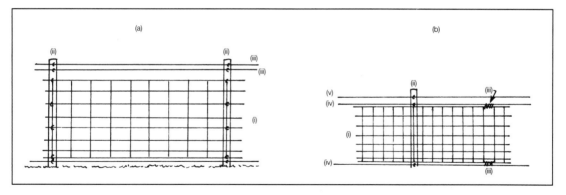

STOCK NETTING

(a) For goats
  (i) Stock netting 1.2m high stapled to each stake
  (ii) Stakes 2.1m × 7.5cm at 2.7m intervals
  (iii) Two separate line-wires strained above netting to increase total fence height to 1.5m

(b) General-purpose for cattle, sheep, lambs
  (i) Stock netting 80cm high (C8/80/15 for lambs, otherwise C8/80/30), *not* stapled to stakes

  (ii) Stakes 1.7m × 10cm at 14m intervals
  (iii) Lashing rods joining netting to line-wires at top and bottom
  (iv) Strained sprung steel line wires
  (v) Separate top line wire to give total fence height of 1m (increase height further if necessary with extra line-wires)

Wrap the beginning of a roll of netting around the starting post and fasten it by stapling, knotting, twisting or linking, as you would with plain wire. If you remove at least the first vertical wire of the netting, you should have ample lengths of horizontal wires to wrap around the post.

Now unroll a length of netting (which is most easily done with the roll laid flat on the ground) until you reach the second straining post. Erect the netting and use temporary rings to the top wire to hold the netting upright while you strain it. Cut off the netting at the straining post and fasten it as before. This is preferable to continuing the run and tight-stapling it to the post as you go, which will weaken the fence. Clearly it would pay to know how long your rolls are so that you can site the straining posts accordingly, allowing for the wrap-around, without wasting time and material by cutting unnecessarily. Most rolls are 50m long, or 100m for HT netting, and it is common practice to join up to as many as six 50m rolls together (depending on the distances between straining posts), while they are laid out flat on the ground, before putting them in place for straining. To join two pieces of

netting in mid-run, use the same techniques as for joining plain wire. If you do not want to cut the netting at a corner post, run the netting *behind* it, that is, on the outside of the boundary.

Lash the netting on top and bottom wires at 2m intervals: lashing rods were specifically designed for woven or welded mesh and are longer lasting and less fiddly than most joining methods, though you could use wire rings or tie-wires, which would be more suitable for the lighter weight of unstrained hexagonal mesh, especially rings, which tend to be pulled open by the weight of woven or welded fencing.

If you are not using line wires to which the netting is attached, you will have to staple the netting to the intermediate stakes. If you are setting hexagonal wire, this extra support will also be needed even if it is attached to strained line wires.

Chestnut paling

Robust but expensive, chestnut paling consists of hand-cleft palings bound together at top and bottom (and middle if necessary) between strong twisted wires. The palings are set closely together, though there is a choice of spacings and of course the wider the spacing, the cheaper.

Set the fence so that the pales are not in contact with the ground; they will then last much longer. Put straining posts at up to 50m apart, and for greater rigidity, strain two line wires between them in the usual way at levels corresponding with those of the paling wires so that they can be attached to each other with gordian knots or flat-metal chainlink netting rings (they look rather like bird leg-rings). Set intermediate stakes every three paces between the straining posts. Lightly strain the paling so that it is taut but not under high tension. Have the snubbed points uppermost to shed rain.

Hurdles

There are two types of hurdle: closely woven wattle panels of hazel, or light, portable sheep gate or bar hurdles made from cleft chestnut, willow, oak or ash. Wattle is used as a screen or windbreak, and was the traditional sheep shelter: shepherds would carry several wattle panels on a pole over their shoulder and take them where they were needed. Hurdles are lighter to carry and were widely used as temporary sheep enclosures, especially for folding the animals on arable crops or for lambing. Ideas on using woven wattles and sheep hurdles to create the snug, old-fashioned type of thatched outdoor lambing yard are given in the Farmyard section.

Wattles are usually tied to stakes at either end by means of tie-wires. The old type always had a square or oblong 'twilly' hole through the panel, more or less centrally, for skewering it on to the carrying pole; it also had long, pointed end 'sails' (uprights) so that it could be simply driven into the ground. Hurdles are erected in the same fashion, and both types are adequate for confining sheep yet light enough to be portable on a man's back. The traditional method of using hurdles for folding was to knock them into position with a heavy mallet (starting a hole with an iron bar on hard or stoney ground), overlapping them so that they could be tied together with

twine at top and bottom. If the fence line was quite long, stakes would be knocked in at intervals to give added support.

Today the manurial value of systematic sheep-folding is less appreciated, and anyway electric fencing has proved to be an easy alternative to hurdles. However, metal hurdles are still used for handling sheep: they make temporary pens in the yard or at shows and markets, though some of the well known sheep fairs still use wooden hurdles and wattles near the coppicing regions of southern England.

Tubular metal hurdles are relatively light and easy to manage; they can be useful hand-carried aids for cornering sheep in a field, for example. There is a perforated disc at the end of one upright: its holes are designed to accept the upright of a neighbouring hurdle so that they are easily linked into straight runs or at any deflected angle you choose.

Brush fencing

Although now usually associated with steeple-chase jumps, brush fencing of a slightly different kind was once a useful, cheap and quick method of enclosure using birch brush (in this country) or cedar brush (in America). Throw up an earth ridge to about a foot above ground level, and drive stakes into it at 2–3ft intervals. Weave the brush in and out of the stakes (like a wattle panel), beating it down firmly into place with a maul to make it as compact as possible. If you leave about a foot of post protruding above the brush, it can be driven down in due course as the embedded foot of the post decays. In theory, the brush will last as long as the stakes, and the whole edifice could last 15–20 years.

A similar woven fence, seen at the Weald and Downland Open Air Museum in Sussex, is made of quite sturdy rods and branches woven in and out of close-set supporting stakes so that it looks like a well laid hedge without the greenery. Such fences often start out green, using fresh-cut branches sappy enough to be supple, and they do give good shelter to young animals in the field or yard.

Strong pleached field-fence at the Weald and Downland Open Air Museum, Singleton.

Post-and-rail fencing

Post-and-rail, although more expensive than wire fencing in terms of materials and skilled labour, has the advantage of being more versatile where the fence run is not straight (it can follow gentle curves or zigzags) and, because of its sectional nature, repairs are generally limited to the damaged section rather than the longer run. A well made rail fence can be visually handsome, too, and less likely to injure or trap livestock but it needs the reinforcement of wire or an electrified scare wire to be really stockproof. A minor disadvantage is that horses seem to enjoy nibbling wooden rails even if you do paint the timber with Jeyes fluid, creosote, old engine sludge, Stockholm tar or some other foul deterrent.

There is no need for the very strong straining posts used in a wire fence: the rigidity of post-and-rail relies on a combination of the innate strength of the material, the firmness and trueness of its uprights and the soundness of the joints between post and rail. The choice in the latter respect is between mortises and nails: mortised joints are stronger and longer lasting but require skilled craftsmanship and are more difficult to manoeuvre. The traditional timber used for mortised fences is oak: the uprights might be sawn or cleft and the rails are usually riven, that is, split rather than sawn, so that they are stronger and longer lasting. The rails of a typical Sussex cleft oak fence are more or less triangular or diamond-shaped in cross-section, with a sharp angle uppermost to shed the rain.

Nailed-rail fences, often of half-round chestnut or sawn treated softwood, are easier and quicker to erect than mortised fences but are more readily dislodged by livestock. Either square or half-round split posts can be used and it is possible to drive them in as long as precautions are taken to protect the post-tops from mallet damage and to ensure that the posts are driven true, with all the faces exactly square to the rails. If in doubt, dig them in instead, especially the main posts at the end of each rail. In many designs, all the posts are 'main' posts because the rails are staggered so that the end-post of a top rail serves as the middle post of a bottom rail. In others the rails form

12.5cm × 7.5cm posts for mortised rails. Designs are numerous and the versatility of the system enables you to design fence sections to suit every situation.

Setting a nailed fence

On a fairly level site with a straight or nicely curved run, it is possible to measure out the post-hole sites accurately (assuming the rails have been accurately cut to length) and

Riven-oak post-and-rail fence.

sections, both top and bottom using the same end posts, with less substantial prick-posts giving rigidity to the centres of the rails.

The simplest traditional nailed post-and-rail fence has 12ft rails, with posts at 6ft intervals. Rail and post dimensions vary according to the fence's role but, typically, rails are about 4cm × 9cm in section if they are sawn, while posts range from half rounds with 10cm faces to more solid

methodically set all or most of the posts and then all the rails, so that in the end the rails flow pleasingly along the line. Stretch a guide line along the run: it can be temporarily staked at points where the fence changes direction or to form a curve. Or, where appropriate, set end-of-run posts and strain a low-level wire between them. Now lay the rails on the ground end to end, and well butted together, to locate the post sites. Mark the sites with a plunge of the crowbar.

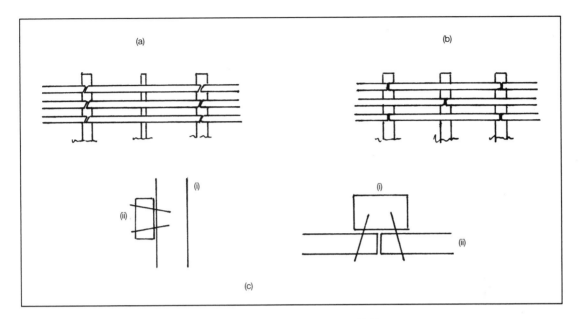

NAILED POST-AND-RAIL FENCING

(a) All rails aligned to same main posts, with centres supported by short stud post
(b) Rails set alternately so that all posts are main posts

(c) Skewing the nails
   (i) Post
   (ii) Rail

However, it is safer to build the fence as you go so that you can be quite sure the posts and rails meet exactly where they should. In many circumstances, this is the only practical possibility anyway.

Dig the post holes as you would for wire-fence straining posts. The posts, rather than the nails, should take the pressure of enclosed livestock so that the rails should be on the stock side of the posts. Set half-round posts with the split face true to the rails; set rectangular sawn posts with the long face to the rails. Make sure that the faces *are* true to the rails so that they do not put stress on them by distortion. Check that the posts are vertical in all planes and true to the general line, and that they are each set to a height above ground that will give you as even a rail run as possible. For example, if the ground is uneven you will need greater length of post above ground in dips and can fill in the low-level gap with wire or an extra rail if necessary, rather than suddenly jagging the level of the whole fence downwards at that point. The rails do not need to run absolutely straight but aim for a reasonably smooth profile: it will look more harmonious, be easier to build, and give a better flush fit between the rail butts.

Use a temporary line (say, a length of string) to give you the levels for the rails, or use a measuring rod to mark where the top of each rail should be on each post. Even if the overall flow of the rails is uneven, aim to have upper and lower rails parallel to each other as far as possible and mark the posts accordingly.

Set the top rail first as it will be the most noticeable. Align it carefully to its mark and nail it at either end, butting closely with its predecessor, and finally nail it to its centre post. Blunt the nail tips first to reduce the risk of splitting the wood unless you can pre-drill it. Use two galvanised nails at each site and drive them offset in order to avoid splitting down the grain of either the rail or the post. For greater security, drive them in at an angle with their tips skewing towards each other.

Where the line changes at an angle or corner, or with a change of slope, it might be necessary to slope-cut or chamfer the rail ends or, in some cases, to cut a rebate in the post itself. Always paint such cuts with a preservative if you are using treated timber.

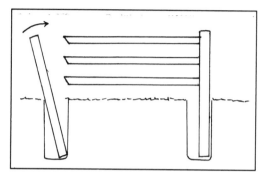

SETTING A MORTISED FENCE

Setting a mortised fence

It is not practicable to set posts in advance. You need to tilt each post to accept the rails, and once the rails are in place the posts are immovable. Run a guide line and dig in the first post firmly, checking its height above ground and that it is vertical and properly aligned, with the mortice holes true to the fence line. (Note that, with rectangular mortise posts, the holes are cut through the longer faces.) Use one of the tapered rails as a measure to site the second post then dig its hole, making the hole wide enough along the fence line so that the post can be tilted to accept the rails. Lean the post in its hole, tipping away from the previous post. Set the rail ends into the mortices on the first post, then ease the second post into position, slotting the other ends of the rails into its holes until they are properly lodged and the post is vertical. Backfill and firm the post, then continue the process down the line.

If a mortised rail needs replacement in due course, it might be difficult to force the posts apart sufficiently to slip in a new rail. Try pushing one end of the new rail as far into its first mortise as it will go, then trim off its other end just to the extent that it overlaps the second post. Nudge the reduced tip into the second mortice, easing it into

position while making sure that enough of the other end of the rail remains in the first mortice to hold it in place. Use wedges if necessary.

Pole fence

If timber is too small to split (e.g. larch thinnings, though these can be rather too whippy to contain larger animals), cut poles about 3 m long. Set posts 2.7 m apart. Shave a flat section at the ends of each pole to make nailing easier, and then nail them to alternative sides of the posts. i.e. with the left hand end of each pole on the outside of its post and the right hand end on the inside of the next post.

'Portable' wooden fencing

Here are some ideas from 19th century America: they are described as portable but are rather cumbersome.

Poultry and pig picket fence

You need sawn timber for this, and it is a good use for old roofing laths. Each 'panel' is independent and its uprights, like those of a wattle hurdle or sheep gate, are pointed for driving into the ground as required. Very simply, the panel consists of three uprights, up to 10 cm thick at the top (in fact they could be ordinary chestnut rounds or splits rather than sawn posts), joined by two rails, at top and bottom, made of, say, 15 cm fence boards. Then nail the laths vertically to the boards so that they project perhaps 25 cm above the upper edge of the top rail. Once the panels are in position as a fence, nail a wide bottom board around the inside of the enclosure to contain pigs or poultry.

American hurdle

This type of fence, or a variation on its theme, used to be seen on every American smallholding. In essence, it avoids the need for driving or digging posts into the ground by using trestles. Each trestle consists of two pieces of timber (sawn or round or split) bolted or nailed together in the form of a high-centred cross and made rigid with a crosspiece near their feet. The crosspiece has a notch at its centre as a resting place for one of the rails of the hurdle: another rail rests in the crotch of the cross. A typical hurdle for such trestles is simply four strips of 2.5 cm board, 3.6 m long and of a width suited to its purpose (the smaller the livestock, the *wider* each board needs to be), nailed to three perpendiculars in such a way that the ends of the horizontals project far enough beyond the outer uprights to hang on the trestle. Take care that the distances between the boards are appropriate so that the bottom of the second and fourth boards fit neatly into the trestle's crotch and crosspiece notch. The more rustic fence uses simple poles rather than board panels and sets each section zigzag to its neighbour.

Electric fencing

A one-wire or two-wire battery-powered fence supported by insulated rods is the most versatile and easily erected temporary livestock deterrent of all. With more powerful fencer units and the use of more substantial wooden posts, electric fences are increasingly being used as permanent stock boundaries

as well. Sheep farmers often used electrified netting, but this has several drawbacks.

Anyone who has touched an electric fence wire knows that the sensation, though brief, is unpleasant enough to deter you from voluntary contact in the future, even through the less 'shocking' medium of a blade of grass held in your fingers. An animal which has been trained to respect an electric fence can develop a psychological aversion to a

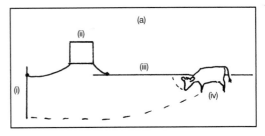

(a) Circuit
  (i) Earthing rod
  (ii) Fencing unit or energiser
  (iii) Fence wire
  (iv) Animal touching the wire completes the circuit by earthing the currrent

ELECTRIC FENCING

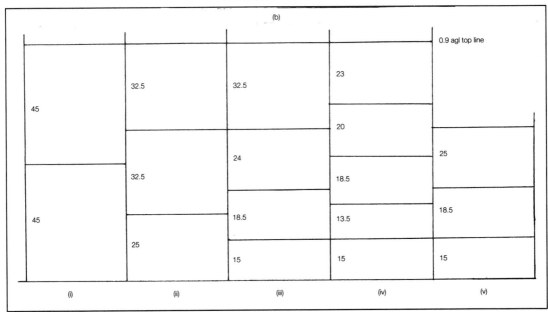

(b) Permanent electric fencing heights
  (i) Cattle (45/45cm)
  (ii) Young cattle (25/32.5/32.5cm)
  (iii) Quiet sheep (15/18.5/24/32.5cm)
  (iv) Sheep and goats (15/13.5/18.5/20/23cm)
  (v) Pigs (15/18.5/25)

79

horizontal wire or string even when there is no charge at all. In the drought of 1976 I grazed a couple of house cows on every available headland around the cornfields with only a stretch of innocent baler twine to keep them off the crop, and not only did they refuse to risk testing the string but also refused to cross its original line for 24 hours or more after it had been removed. Pigs, likewise, often refuse to cross the 'ghost line' and indeed this is one of the drawbacks of electric fencing. It can be almost impossible to drive a sensitive animal through a legitimate gap in an electric fence or across where the fence used to be.

However, some animals are quick to appreciate that failed fencer batteries or shorting gives them immunity to the wire, and that thick fleeces are good insulators, or that they can jump over or roll under without touching the wire itself. Yet others won't risk even stepping over a low line of electrified wires: they seem to imagine that the power stretches upwards infinitely.

The essence of training stock to respect electric fencing is to ensure that their first contact with it is tentatively, with their moist, tender muzzles. Try putting a wisp of dry, sweet hay on the wire, or getting someone to stand with a food lure just beyond the wire — but not someone who will be handling the stock because the animals might connect the shock with the person rather than the wire and will develop an aversion to them. Some fencing units have a choice of high or low settings: use the former for training.

Energisers
The electric current, whether originating from a battery or from the mains, is transformed by the fencing unit or 'energiser' to a much higher voltage but the charge is emitted in pulses so that the animal, human or otherwise, has a chance to withdraw from contact between each pulse. The effect is greater at higher voltages and when the ground is wet (the earthing rod should be in wet ground) but less on stoney ground or through horns, fleeces or rubber soles. Electric fences work by using the animal to complete an electric circuit by earthing it: the components of the circuit are a power source, conducting fence wire, the animal, the ground, the earthing rod and back to the power source or fencing unit. The whole system can be jeopardised if the current is inadvertently partially earthed by contact with lush vegetation along the fence line, which will reduce its effectiveness, and more high-powered modern fencing units deal with this situation by burning off the growth.

There is a wide range of units and their scope is affected by the gauge, length and number of wires in the fence and also by climate and vegetation. In theory, up to 12 miles of single-line fence can be electrified with either mains or 12 volt battery units, with the latest massively powered units capable of energising well over 40,000 m of wire — the equivalent of more than 25 miles. Lower-output 12 volt battery fencers can energise from half a mile in the smallest. Simple battery systems are ideal for temporary fencing (for example, folding or rotational grazing) as the whole system is light to move, quick to erect and initially cheap to buy. The battery unit is independent of mains supplies and is easily transported to the site as it weighs only a few pounds.

Typical older battery fencers make a ticking sound and nearly all types have pulsating lights to warn you that the system is live and to give evidence that the battery is still working. Some animals learn to associated the ticking with the fence's effectiveness and take advantage when the ticking stops. It is important to keep a check on the battery, to ensure that all supporting posts are well insulated from the wires and to keep conductors such as long grasses well clear of the wire (bearing in mind that rain can bend otherwise out-of-reach stems into contact). Be very careful with high-powered battery energisers: they can be dangerous if faulty and can even become lethal. Whatever type of energiser you use, make sure that the public is aware of an electrified fence: put up warning signs and insulate access points on public rights of way. And remember that a plain steel wire is hard to see at the best of times, and just about invisible in poor light at dawn or dusk. (Here speaks a flattened early morning jogger!)

For permanent fencing, or for substantial distances, you will need a mains-powered energiser installed by a competent electrician, with very careful attention to the manufacturer's instructions regarding earthing and the length and type of lead-out wires.

Safety points

Whatever type of energiser is used, bear the following safety points in mind when setting up an electric fence:

★ Do not attach the lines to electricity supply posts.

★ If there are power lines in the area, do not run the fence more than 2m above ground level and only pass it below the power lines at right angles, never parallel to them or to a telephone line.

★ Never use more than one energiser on a fence line.

★ If separate lines are on separate energisers, keep the fences at least 2m apart at all points.

★ Where there is a public right of way, put signs warning that the fence is electric, and insulate gates and stiles. If the line must cross a public road, it must go underground or be at least 5m above the road and you must consult the highways authority in advance.

★ On no account electrify barbed-wire, either by design or by default. Imagine what will happen when an animal or person gets entangled with the stuff.

Posts

Electric fencing wires need to be taut to be fully effective and you therefore need a reasonably sturdy support system at run ends and turning points to take a certain amount of strain, though it will not be much for simple temporary fencing. Intermediate posts can be very lightweight and as much as 10–12m apart: their role is to keep the wires horizontal and they do not need to take any strain from either the wire's tension or the pressure of livestock. With permanent fencing using modern high-powered energisers and HT wire, there can be even greater distances between the intermediates — say 40m if droppers are used at 10m intervals.

For temporary fencing, use pigtail posts: these are steel rods with or without a simple foot tread for instant stamping into the ground (and added stability) and with a plastic insulation loop at the top to carry the wire, either as part of the post or bought separately. You can also buy butterfly insulators which can be screwed round the rod at suitable heights to carry extra lines, and there are several other designs of insulator. There are various pre-formed plastic stakes with hooks for the wires at several heights, while electric sheep netting is usually supplied complete with its own plastic push-in stakes.

Corner, turning and end or straining posts can be tripod pigtail posts or ordinary chestnut stakes driven in 45cm and strutted against the line of the wire's strain. For a semi-permanent fence, you could use 5cm poles of locally available wood such as hazel or larch, with nail-on or screw-on insulators. Some people use plastic baler twine to good effect to keep a wire clear of a metal or wooden post, especially at turning points, where the twine is also used for adjusting strain.

Proper permanent fences need more lasting supports. Use sturdier, round straining posts and set them about 200m apart. There are several types of insulator suitable for straining posts including strong porcelain 'eggs', or insulator pads which fit a hole drilled right through the post (they also grip the strained wire) or insulated strain tubes. Remember that the wire might stretch in warm weather and thus become slack and less effective: ensure that it is possible to re-strain it easily so that it remains efficient. Porcelain eggs connected to the post by non-electric wire ties or strong plastic twine can be readily drawn closer to a corner post to increase the strain, for example, or you could use an insulated reel system.

Access

It might be necessary to carry a wire safely across existing gateways, either by burying it encased in a plastic pipe (use non-corrosive, double-insulated, galvanised wire) or by carrying it overhead, high enough to be well clear of people, animals, vehicles and equipment.

Regular access points in simple electrified fences usually consist of a single line of electrified wire attached to an end post at one side of the gap and with an insulated handle at the other side which hooks to the other end post. This type of gateway often uses a coiled spring of HT wire which can stretch across the gap. For a public right of way, use insulating tubes or lengths of polythene pipe to enclose the wire at a stile. Consult your supplier for other ideas.

Incidentally, there is now an imaginative system of using buried electric fencing, originally designed to train a dog to stay within its garden boundaries but recently adapted for small flocks of sheep on public land. Each animal wears a special responder which ensures that it receives a mild shock if it passes over the buried wire. As long as the boundaries are permanent, the animal quickly learns to respect its limits.

Electric netting

Polywire-and-plastic electric netting can be useful as a temporary sheep enclosure: it is completely flexible, very light and portable, but it is quite fragile and easily tangled. It can also trap unwary livestock who tend to push their heads through the netting, especially if the power fails. Young sheep can virtually throttle themselves and horned animals get into a terrible tangle as they try to withdraw their heads. The mesh can literally garotte a lamb, slice the hoof off a careless horse or panic a trapped deer to death.

Electric sheep-netting for flexible orchard grazing. *(Anna Oakford)*.

Combined fencing

A line of electric wire can reinforce other fencing systems. For example, it can be used as an extra top or bottom line with field fencing or stock netting (but not connected to the netting) or as one or two lines of otherwise non-electric multi-line wire fences. More particularly, it finds a role as a *scare wire* set a few inches in front of a fence, wall or pen to deter the adventurous — either to keep retained animals in or to keep curious predators out, especially foxes investigating a chicken run. Set the scare wire at a level appropriate to the target animal and its habits: usually about two-thirds of the animal's height so that the nose meets the wire first. Use commercial offset brackets or insulators attached to existing uprights, or set a separate line of short wooden posts.

The Fieldguard system

This French system, invented in 1983 and initially designed for horses but suitable for a wide range of livestock, uses highly visible tapes rather than wires to carry the current. The system includes indestructible glass-fibre stakes and special insulators which grip the tape tightly so that it does not chafe when the wind blows. Detailed installation instructions are available in the distributor's excellent and comprehensive booklets (see Addresses), which also give lots of intriguing ideas for using the system as a handling aid, including everything from tree guards to circular lunging pens and travelling paddocks, and as an aid to catch and load horses or to cure crib-biters.

The tape is in fact a mesh, specially designed to allow wind to blow through it and reduce stress on the fence as long as it is not overstrained. There are three different widths and a choice of colours for different situations. For example, the narrow 12.5mm close-weave, which is the cheapest, can be used for cattle, sheep or docile pigs; the medium 20mm (wide or close-weave) for outdoor pigs; and the stronger 40mm wide for single-strand cattle or pig fencing and as a two-run fence for horses. The colours at present include white (for visibility), brown, or red-and-green. The visual impact of the tape is important: it seems to be a much more effective psychological barrier than wire, especially with flight-prone animals like horses.

The system can be used with most of the usual energisers, but is best with the more powerful types: the distributors will be glad to give advice. There is also a good range of associated equipment. The main drawback to the system (apart from the fact that it has only been in use for a few years) is the initial cost: tape is of course more expensive than a simple wire but horse owners will appreciate its benefits and it is also claimed that virtually every outdoor pig farm in Sweden now uses the system.

Dry-stone walls

A well-built wall, with regular maintenance at the first sign of weakness, should outlast a dozen fences and it is therefore well worth spending extra time and effort on its construction. The foundation of a good stone wall is perfect drainage: there should be no standing water on the ground surface along its line, nor any as deep as frost will penetrate underground. For a new wall, if necessary dig out a good drainage ditch to below frost level to keep water away from the line and fill it with small broken stones.

The second essential is to use stones with relatively flat surfaces, or which can be shaped so, as they will lie more snugly and are less likely to be unsettled by frosts. The type of stone naturally depends on local availability.

There are many regional variations in wall structure but the main components of a good wall are its foundation stones, its two sides (built so that the wall tapers slightly as it rises), binding or through stones at intervals for stability, and a filling of small stones in the cavity to prevent the two sides from collapsing inwards. Single-sided walls are much less stable than doubles, of course, and are perhaps best relegated to 'stone hedges', which are earth banks faced with stone on the outside and capped with stones, turf or brushwood.

The width of the foundation depends on the type of stone used and the proposed height of the wall. Quarried stone is much easier to use and shape than boulders and is more stable so that it needs less foundation width but any substantial wall of, say, the traditional 4ft 6in high (1.4m) requires a lower stratum at least 0.6m wide and preferably 0.7–0.8m. A 5ft wall (1.5m — and it needs to be at least that tall to contain upland sheep) merits a foundation width of at least 0.7m. If there is plenty of stone to hand, make the foundation as wide as possible — 0.9m or more. No wall should be less than 0.3m wide at its top, and any decrease in width from base to top should be gradual.

If the line of the wall runs down a hill, dig a series of steps at ground level so that each foundation stone (and preferably all the other tiers) lies horizontally level. If the line is across a slope, again the stones must be laid horizontal rather than parallel to the slope.

Begin by setting a pair of guide strings along the line and dig out a trench down to the subsoil — perhaps 10–15cm deep. Remove any projecting stones and leave the bed of the trench level and firm. Your work will be easier if the trench is wider than the foundation layer, and so your next task is to re-set the guide strings to the foundation width and about 20–30cm above ground level so that there is enough space beneath them

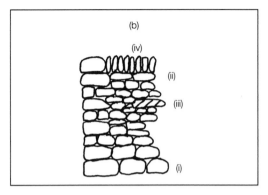

(b) Side view of wallhead
  (i) Foundation stones
  (ii) Building stones
  (iii) Throughstone
  (iv) Coping stones

for the first tier of the wall. As you build you will be shifting the lines upwards so that they are always a little above the current tier. Build the two sides of the wall simultaneously.

Put down the largest, squarest stones for the foundation layer or footings. Set them with their broadest, flattest surfaces face down to spread the weight of the wall and keep them from sinking. Align their outer faces precisely along the strings and butt them as close to each other as possible, using a crowbar and stone-hammer to knock off awkward protrusions for a snug fit. Pack any gaps between the two rows with small stones.

As you build the wall up, the aim is to lay each stone in such a way that the wall is firmly bound together as a whole, and that of course entails overlapping subsequent tiers in brick-bonding style, so that each joint is capped by the stone above it. Stones which are more oblong than square should be set with their shorter flat faces on the outside of the wall so that their length helps to bind them into the wall's depth. Set them flat, or tilting slightly down to the outside face to shed rainwater, and add small-stone fill as you go.

At certain levels (probably in only one or perhaps two tiers in the whole wall) include substantial binder stones, laid across the wall on a level base and reaching from one

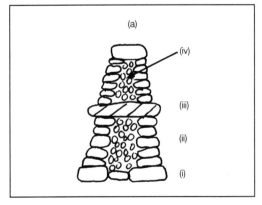

(a) Section through wall
  (i) Large foundation stones
  (ii) Building stones
  (iii) Throughstone
  (iv) Small stones for infilling

side to the other, perhaps protruding slightly on each side. Set them as often as available materials allow, for greater strength, and not more than a stride apart. If there is a second tier of binders, place the stones so that they alternate with those of the first.

The size of the sides' stones can be reduced as the wall rises but only gradually: keep them of a good size in general. However, increase their size towards the top for a better looking finish, and finally top the whole wall with a layer of thin capping stones in keeping with local customs. These capping or coping stones give the wall a finished look and also act as binders to give it added stability: they are often quite thin but are placed upright rather than flat so that they add plenty of weight.

At the end of a length of wall (for example, a gateway) build a wall-head using through-stones set alternately with long stones at right angles to them and going back into the length of the wall. If you want to incorporate sheep creep-holes through the wall as you build it, use good large lintel stones to bridge the gaps. You can also build in stone stiles with steps for easy access.

In some cases the effectiveness of an existing wall as a livestock or wildlife barrier is increased by adding two or three lines of wire to give the wall greater height. Walls are often on stony ground so that it is not easy to knock in fencing posts along the line; in any case, if the posts are set into the ground at the foot of the wall they will probably lean and eventually dislodge some of the stones. If it does seem practicable to drive them into the ground, set them on the stock side of the wall, strutting them at corners if necessary; or knock them into the ground as far as possible but leaning along the slope of the wall, then bind them by running wires through the wall, round the post and back through the wall for fixing to battens on the far side. The battens can be twisted to tighten the grip of the wires.

However, these methods use posts which are much longer than is required for the job of supporting top lines of wire and a common alternative is to set flat metal support bars a little way into the top of the wall, with holes drilled through them for the wires. End-of-the-run bars would need the support of flat metal struts against the strain of the wire, and at this point the wire is attached to eye-bolts which can be tightened to adjust the tension when necessary.

Fencing supports can be built into a new wall during its construction. Use a hollow concrete block (or a stone with a hole chiselled through it) to take the foot of the post, which is secured there with mortar, then set the block or stone complete with its post into the wall as you build, at perhaps halfway up the wall, laying it across like a binder.

Hedges

'The hawthorn,' to quote from *Baxter's Library of Agricultural and Horticultural Knowledge* published in the 1830s, 'on account of the stiffness of its branches, the sharpness of its thorns, and its capability of bearing the severest winters without injury, is universally preferred to all other trees for hedges, and may be so managed as to present a barrier to all kinds of cattle, and not to be passed, without difficulty, even by such persons as might attempt to intrude upon the grounds of others. Though fences, both durable and elegant, might be constructed at comparatively small expense, yet how few fields, and still fewer plantations, do we pass without seeing them exposed to the ravages of all kinds of cattle! A mock ditch, a ragged and rotten hedge, or a broken wall, being in too many instances the only barrier to defend valuable property from the inroads of every browsing animal.'

New hedges

Baxter's magnificent manual was published, in several editions, during a period when English agriculture was undergoing radical changes — an exciting time with major developments in husbandry of all kinds, and even the old art of hedge-planting and maintenance was being improved. The book describes that the 'common practice' had been to plant young hawthorn trees in a straight line, four to six inches apart, either on an embankment or, if the drainage was suitable, on the level; they would be pruned back three or four times before being allowed to 'throw out for good', with the first pruning almost to ground level and each succeeding one six to eight inches above the last in order to make the plants thick at the bottom. Thereafter they would be cut regularly twice a year with a 'switching bill' (which was like a large pruning knife with a handle two to four feet long), in order to 'hog-mane' them so that they were narrower at the top and sloping gradually at the sides.

However, a new and improved method had become established in the best hedge districts, and in essence it can still be used today:

1. Work out the proposed line of the hedge and make an embankment along it by throwing up earth excavated from a ditch. (Traditionally, you can tell to which property a hedge belongs by which side the ditch lies: one would throw up the excavated soil to one's own side of the boundary.) The ditch sides should be equally sloped and it should be 30 cm wide at its base, regardless of depth. Make the bank so that the plants, when set upon it, will have a 'slight inclination upwards': invert a sod 12–15 cm thick and broader than the spade, laying it grass to grass along the guide line and then paring it and beating it down to form a slope to support the buried part of the plant.

2. Choose plants with a good, fibrous root system, preferably those which have been transplanted twice in the nursery. Before planting, prune off the top of the stem to within 12–15 cm above the roots, using a sharp implement to make a good clean cut with an upward slant. Plant in winter when soil conditions are neither too frosty nor too wet. Set each plant along the slope of the inverted turf, with their cut end protruding 2–3 cm beyond the sod towards the ditch. Now build up a good mound over the lower part of the plant, including a heap of compost, leafmould or well-rotted manure just beyond the roots (away from the ditch) to encourage good growth. Finish off the mound so that it is smooth, with a slightly flattened top.

3. For the first three or four years after planting, keep the bed weeded and add more earth to the mound as needed. Take great pains with pruning, which determines the eventual value of the hedge: time it for late autumn, very early spring or midsummer (not late spring) and switch off all branches which straggle over the ditch but leave those which grow towards the bank. Very little pruning should be needed in the first year. Of course the plants will need protection from browsing animals until they are well enough established to fend for themselves.

The *Smallholder's Encyclopaedia*, published shortly after the Second World War, emphasises the importance of regular trimming throughout the life of a hedge to encourage it to become bushy and retain its ability to deter stock even at the base. It suggested that a new hedge should be encouraged to grow well by mulching it with manure on the surface of the ground; the new plants should be cut back to almost ground level in December or January of their second year and thereafter the sides should be trimmed as growth develops but the tops or leading shoots should not be cut back until they have completed each season's growth, at which stage they can be taken back to the required hedge height. This book recommends side-trimming three times a year while the hedge is becoming established.

Today most hedges are planted in double rows, in which the plants are staggered to give greater density at the base. They can be set in a trench about 30 cm wide, or in two slightly narrower trenches 15 cm apart; however, in good soils in a single row will probably suffice. Nor is the choice limited to thorn, though it is still one of the most effective and quick-growing barriers. Baxter recommended holly hedges to protect ewes and their lambs or, in exposed situations on thin, chalky soil or where rabbits and hare were a nuisance, buckthorn because of its bitter taste, rapid growth and mass of fibrous roots able to make the best of dry soils. (It helps in such situations to form a slight dip in the bank to hold available moisture as long as possible.)

Every farm, states Baxter, should have a small piece of good ground laid out in three-foot beds planted with thorn, holly, maple, crabstocks and buckthorn ready to be transplanted into gaps in old hedges or to make new ones: indeed old banks tend to become 'hedgesick' and it is often better to pull them down and start afresh, with a different species. Apparently elm will grow better after oak than will oak after oak, if elm will still grow at all.

Thorns can be propagated quite easily from seed, if you are patient enough to wait for germination, or you can set 5–12 cm root cuttings from healthy plants. The *Encyclopaedia* recommends thorn as the most reliable hedging plant of all but suggests that holly or the thorny myrobalan plum are also suitable barriers for stock. Other possible hedging species include beech, hornbeam, lime, field maple, hazel, dogwood, gorse (which tends to develop gaps), spindle (a host plant for aphids) or various willows if the ground is wet, but really any livestock hedge is best with plenty of thorn in it, even if several other species are incorporated for the variety which wildlife appreciates. 'Thorn' includes blackthorn, which blossoms on bare twigs and later bears sloes, and the more common quickthorn which, also known as hawthorn or may, blossoms after its young leaves have unfolded. Be guided by local practice when choosing hedging species, especially in difficult situations such as coastal environments, and make quite sure you avoid poisonous species such as box, broom, cherry laurel, cupressus, laburnum, rhododendron and yew.

Above all, don't be tempted to buy an instant hedge of older plants but use those which are perhaps 3–4 years old, sturdily grown and healthy. A well developed root system is much more important than a lot of top growth. Treat each plant as carefully as you would a specimen tree, bearing in mind that good hedges can last a great deal longer in the landscape than individual trees and deserve very thorough ground preparation and careful planting.

Hedge-trimming

The most common tractor-powered farm hedge cutter today is the flail — a high-speed flail rotor on the end of a hydraulic arm so that the height, distance and angle of the cutter is very versatile. It can trim sides and tops of hedges, or the sides of banks and ditches. It makes a distastrous mess on larger stems, leaving them hideously ragged and wide open to disease, but is more capable of getting through them than are conventional cutters with reciprocating knife-bars. The bar cutter makes a much tidier job of a hedge which has been trimmed regularly, before its twigs become too thick. The most beautifully cut hedges have been hand-trimmed with a hook by those who know how to use one.

The most common hedge profile is rectangular, which is simple to trim but not necessarily the most useful: given a rounded top it would have greater strength under the weight of snow, for example, but would then need to be hand-trimmed or cut with hand-held power tools. A much better hedge for wildlife would be A-shaped, and decidedly taller than the usual metre-high roadside hedge. Nesting birds would appreciate a hedge twice as high and the A-shape gives a thicker hedge bottom (to deter adventurous sheep) and makes a more effective windbreak, with less likelihood of turbulence. It also encourages you to leave good hedgerow saplings intact.

For the sake of wildlife, trim hedges after the autumn berries have served their purpose but before birds begin to nest. For the sake of the hedge, do not cut it in times of heavy frost. If your hedge-cutting is drastic, consider doing it in stages so that beneficial insects wintering in the hedge have a chance to find new accommodation.

Hedge-laying

Even the most diligently trimmed hedge will in due course begin to thin, especially at the base, so that it is no longer stockproof. To make it good again, lay it. Hedge-laying is

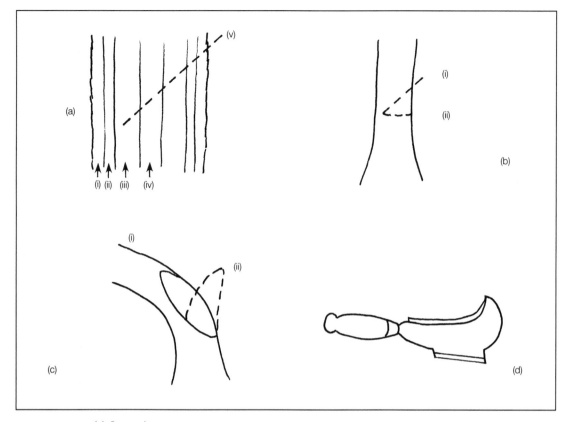

(a) Layers in a stem
  (i) Bark
  (ii) Cambium
  (iii) Sapwood
  (iv) Heartwood
  (v) Extent and angle of cut (45 degrees or sharper)

(b) The cut
  (i) Diagonal cut downwards with billhook or axe
  (ii) For the inexpert: first cut horizontally with saw about three-quarters through stem

(c) Bending the pleacher at an acute angle to the ground (45 degrees or less); projecting stub cleanly removed

(d) Billhook: one of many regional styles

the art of encouraging new growth from existing stems in the base of the hedge by almost severing them with a sharply angled cut and then persuading them to lie at an acute angle to the ground so that, like the horizontal stems of climbing roses, they send out new shoots from the old wood. And it *is* an art: you would be well advised to seek out a local hedge-layer who has many years of experience rather than trying to lay a hedge yourself.

Very basically, the main stems are cut through to the point where they are easily bent down (laid) but still retain sufficient cambium to sustain them. There are various regional methods of keeping them laid, with patterns of interweaving and binding. Then they will need protecting from livestock until the plants have bushed out adequately. The National Hedgelaying Society can give advice and publishes a useful small book; the subject is covered in much greater depth in the Hedging book produced by BTCV (British Trust for Conservation Volunteers), including comprehensive details of different regional techniques and styles.

The main steps are these. Clear the hedgerow of weeds, rubbish, old wire and so on and repair the bank if necessary, then choose the main stems you want to retain as pleachers and remove all their side-shoots. Use sharp implements (billhook, axe or perhaps a saw) to cut accurately and cleanly into each pleacher at an angle of about 45 degrees, making quite sure you leave an intact lifeline strip of bark, cambium and a little sapwood so that the top of the plant can still thrive. The intention is to be able to bend the cut pleacher easily without either splitting it (if you have not cut far enough) or penetrating the cambium (if the cut is too long) and you should aim to finish the cut about three-quarters of the way through the stem. The remaining strip also needs to be strong enough not to give way under the weight of other pleachers which will be laid on top, and it needs to be protected from the stress of being twisted. The most delicate part of the art of hedgelaying is the next step: gently bend the pleacher over without damaging that lifeline, so that it lies between perhaps 25–45 degrees above horizontal (sap does not run downhill, so do not bend it further down than horizontal). Trim off the protruding tongue of wood which resulted from the diagonal cut, leaving a clean, smooth surface which can shed the rain rather than collect it. Use stakes here and there along the hedge and weave the tips of the pleachers among them as you proceed, and finally bind the top of the whole laid hedge according to local custom, perhaps with thin hazel or willow withies or using crook-ended stakes. Make it all look neat and tidy so that you can display your work with pride.

Recently a farmer in Wiltshire devised a method of 'mechanised hedge-laying', especially for converting overgrown hedges (effectively shelter belts with trees up to 4.5m tall) into stockproof hedges. All upright branches and stems are cut at a 45 degree angle with a chainsaw at about 0.3m from

Experienced hedge-layer at work in Lincolnshire.
(Anna Oakford).

ground level, the cuts penetrating three-quarters of the way through the wood. Then the back of a digger bucket on a JCB is used to lay the cut stems along the hedge line — and that's it. Rather brutal, and hardly a craft.

Willow walls

Willow, in the right situation, grows very fast indeed and can be used for quick hedging in several ways. Osier cuttings set as a hedge can grow several feet in one summer (and can then be pollarded to provide fodder for goats and sheep) and take easily in moist soils. Crack willow (*Salix fragilis*) regenerates very readily from broken twigs: cut young stems from mature willows in June, trim them into yard-long rods removing all leaves and side growths, and plunge the lower quarter of the stems in a silty garden pond: they will sprout roots in a week or so. Transplant them to the hedge line in autumn and rub off any out-pointing buds to encourage the shoots to grow along the line, when they can be woven into a living wattle fence. Alternatively, push willow rods into the soil in two parallel lines 1.7 m apart and at 50 cm intervals, leaving about a metre of pole protruding but plenty of it in the ground and with the tips slightly inclined towards the opposite row. Weave a wattle around these using cut stems 2.5 cm in diameter and about 3.5 m long. Fill the gap between the two wattle walls with soil, keeping it moist so that the woven willow can root into it and become a living willow wall.

Access

Consider why access through a boundary is needed and then plan ahead. For example, implements and trailers can be wider than the tractor which draws them, so that tractor access points are now usually nearer 12 ft (say 3.5 m) than 9 ft wide and are also sited and designed to avoid problems in manoeuvring equipment through them. Allow 5 m for something like a baler — and that width of access is enough to need double gates. Also consider that gateways in some situations might need to give access to emergency vehicles; a fire engine is wider than the family car and needs an access width of at least 3 m.

Access to and from livestock areas needs special thought and can sometimes be combined with a handling system for convenience, or at least designed to funnel stock in the right direction. In some situations a double gating system is merited so that a group of animals can be penned in a holding area at the access point (which is useful for loading and several routine management operations) and also so that there is less chance of an escape when, say, a tractor needs to enter the field or when a lone person is trying to return a couple of escapees without letting out the stay-at-homes.

Bear in mind that some animals, especially sheep and rooting pigs, are quick to take advantage of a promising escape route *under* a gate and that constant traffic can erode the gateway and create a convenient dip for adventurers which might also become an accidental exit for calves: they sometimes lie down next to a gate or fence for a doze and find themselves on the other side without quite knowing how. Use something like chalk to build up the surface in the dip, which will also help to reduce poaching (i.e. the churning up of wet ground at a popular venue because of the continual congregation of hooved animals), or attach a wire mesh apron to the base of the gate.

It really is worth investing a little extra in an access which can be opened and closed *easily* when necessary. It is all too easy to let old gates fall into disrepair and tie them together with baler twine, or to prop up a hurdle or some other makeshift barrier like a couple of lines of barbed-wire — all of which will make you curse every time you use the gateway. Like making the effort to create sound fencing from the start, investing in reasonably efficient access barriers will pay in the long run, in the coinage of time and frustration if nothing else.

There are countless types of barrier but basically they fall into the following categories:
★ Simple removable lines of plain wire or lengths of netting or hurdles.
★ Slip-rails and slip-gates.
★ Hung gates (wooden or metal).
★ Rights-of-way stiles.
★ Cattle grids and moats.

Wire gates

A few strands of plain wire (never barbed — it could too easily wrap around and cause injury) can be stapled to a light, free-standing post, with an extra intermediate post or two for support if the gap is wide. To close the gate, the free post is looped to an end-of-run fence post by wire or twine, both at the top and at the bottom. This type of gate is cheap and simple, but awkward to use as it is so collapsible; it is also difficult to leave ajar when necessary, unless there is a spare post against which it can be hooked back.

Stock netting can be used on the same principle to make a more stockproof wire

Larch poles as slip-rails supported in U-bolts to create access, combined with open-air paved milking area and handling pen for house cows.

Lightweight metal yard gate with young Highland cattle. Mesh at the base prevents very young animals from finding themselves on the wrong side of the gate.

gate without it needing to be electrified. At its simplest, a length of netting is stapled round one end-of-run post, stapled again to a free intermediary and finally round a second free post at the far end, which is looped at top and foot to the opposite end-of-run post. The gate will be more secure if a crank hook is used instead of the top loop.

Slips

Round or sawn rails across a gateway can be slipped into simple iron U or D bolts hammered into end-of-run posts — perhaps the easiest and cheapest permanent gate of all. To prevent the rails being dislodged by livestock (who tend to use them as neck scratchers), drill vertical holes in the ends of the rails and drop long removable coach bolts into them: to open the gateway, simply lift out the bolts, but have them attached to the rail by a short piece of chain so that you don't drop them in the long grass.

If the gateway is wide enough for a tractor, the rails will need supporting at the centre. Dig a hole for a removable centre post and line it with concrete so that the post can easily be lifted out or replaced. The post will no doubt swell when it is wet and could become difficult to remove: give it a couple of handles for easy gripping (U bolts again, perhaps, which will also act as rail supports) and make sure the concreted hole is large enough to allow for the wood's expansion and has drainage holes.

A slip gate works on the same principles but is more substantial. It is a complete, rigid panel — either plain boards or perhaps a sheep hurdle — with protruding top and bottom rails to hang by. The protrusions slide between horizontal bars at right angles to the access, nailed between the end-of-run post and an extra post set a short distance from it, with a similar arrangement at the other end of the gateway. This hanging system is rather stronger than U-bolts.

Hung gates

Wooden gates are traditional, handsome, reparable and long-lasting (if made of hardwood such as oak) but they are expensive to buy and they are heavy: they need hefty

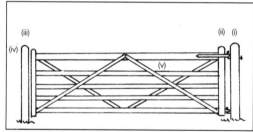

(a) Parts of a gate
  (i) Hanging post
  (ii) Hanging stile or heel
  (iii) Shutting stile or head
  (iv) Shutting or slamming post
  (v) Brace

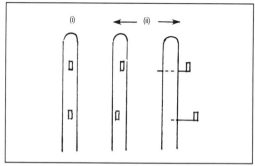

(b) Setting the gate hooks
  (i) Centred for balanced gate
  (ii) Offcentred for self-closing gate

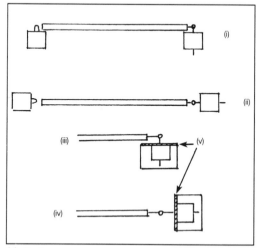

(c) Posts
  (i) Gate set behind posts: opens 180 degrees in one direction
  (ii) Gate set between posts: swings both ways
  (iii) Post-hole for (i), with post set against undisturbed face (v)
  (iv) Post-hole for (iii)

gateposts sunk well into the ground in order to take the weight and remain plumb. The traditional five-bar gate was 10ft wide; in metric terms a standard agricultural five-barred gate is 3.6m wide. Note that the diagonal brace is designed to run from the foot of the hanging stile up to the top rail: don't set your gate upside-down or you will transfer the thrust to the top of the hanging post.

Metal gates are made of galvanised tubular metal and are lightweight, cheaper to buy, easy to install and can span a wider gap as a single gate. The main problems with a wide span are that a metal gate could begin to buckle if it is climbed and it will need plenty of space to accommodate its length throughout the opening arc. Metal gates are usually sold complete with latches, hanging-eyes and hooked hanging-posts, whereas the 'furniture' for wooden gates is usually extra and can be quite costly.

Posts

Every gate has two posts. The shutting or slamming post stands beside the gate's shutting stile or head when it is closed and takes very little stress from the gate but it needs to be stable so that it remains true for the gate's latching system. The hanging post, which takes the full weight of the suspended gate, needs to be particularly robust. Wooden posts should be of hardwood or pressure-treated softwood, with 'weathered' (sloped) or metal-capped tops to shed rainwater. The hole for the hanging-post of a wooden gate should be at least 1m deep and the top of the post should project about 5cm above the top of the gate's hanging stile or heel. The sunken part of the post should be set with its straining face against the undisturbed face of the hole for greatest stability and it should stand plumb vertical from every aspect. Set the post before attaching any fittings to it. Do not be tempted to hang gates from fence straining posts but have separate gate posts so that the gate and fence are independent and do not distort each other.

Rides

Rides are fitted to the gate and will be slotted over the gatepost hooks. The top ride on a wooden gate has much longer arms than the bottom one as it will take more weight. On a level site, the eyes of the two rides will be aligned directly one above the other; on slopes, or for self-closing gates, they can be offset. Special rising-hinges lift a gate as it is opened, if this is required on awkward ground.

Hooks

A wooden gate's hinges hang on hooks set on the hanging-post. There are various designs. Usually the bottom hook is simply driven into the post (it is best to drill a pilot hole first, but make it a tight fit) but the top hook, which takes most of the gate's weight, has a longer shank which passes right through the post and is secured on the far side with a bolt so that the amount it projects can be adjusted. Make sure that the holes are drilled horizontally for a true hang. Hooks for lighter gates are fixed by a screw-on plate.

Hooks on metal posts are integral to the post and it is therefore necessary to set the post to precisely the right height in the ground. Measure the height of the gate's bottom eye to its lowest point and add 5cm for ground clearance, then measure and mark the same distance on the post as its ground level. Be equally careful in measuring the shutting post, though unlike the hanging post this need not be concreted into position.

Hanging a gate

If you hang a gate between its posts, it can be opened both ways but will bind against the hanging post in due course; in most circumstances gates are designed to open one way only, and are hung behind their posts so that they can open a full 180 degrees. Gates should open *into* livestock areas and should preferably be hung so that they are self-closing.

Gate hanging is something of an art. The aim in many situations is for the gate to hang in balance, so that it will remain in whatever position it is left when open. On a level site with an absolutely perpendicular post (an important factor), this will mean that the two post hooks which take the hinges of a wooden gate are set in line with each other, one directly above the other in a vertical plane. Set the bottom hook first, and allow for adequate ground clearance for the heel of the gate as it is opened. Measure the site for the upper hook, making sure that the distance between the hooks corresponds exactly with that between the rides on the gate itself.

If you deliberately want a self-closing swing to the gate, or if the gateway is on a slope, set the hanging post plumb vertical but offset the hanging hooks in two planes, as shown in the diagrams, in order to tilt the weight of the gate.

Both hooks are normally fitted facing upwards so that the gate is simply lifted on to them. However, it is just as simply lifted off, in which case padlocks become irrelevant. To prevent this sort of vandalism, invert the top hook but fit its ride to the hook *before* bolting it to the gate rail's pre-drilled holes.

Those who enjoy a challenge might like the idea of homemade wooden hinges. The most rough-and-ready is the pin-post: the hanging stile is hewn at top and bottom so that each end is peglike. The hanging post is

a section of small tree-trunk carefully chosen so that a branch, cut to a stub of appropriate length, acts as the top hook: a hole is drilled through it for the stile's top peg, The bottom peg pivots in a hole gouged out of a log buried in the ground.

Latches
Here again, the choice is wide. The simplest latch is a swing-over loop, fitted on the shutting or slamming post and of either metal or chain but preferably not baler twine! It is easily opened — by intelligent livestock as well as humans. There are also all sorts of lever or spring latches, among them some automatic self-latching devices which are often rather fiddly to use, especially if your fingers are cold.

On metal gates the latches are integral to the gate and are usually simple sliding bolts (which must, of course, align precisely with the receiver on the gatepost and which can be stiff to operate) or automatic catches. Double metal gates have loop-overs, a system also used for double wooden gates, which usually need drop-bolts into the ground as well to keep the gates closed.

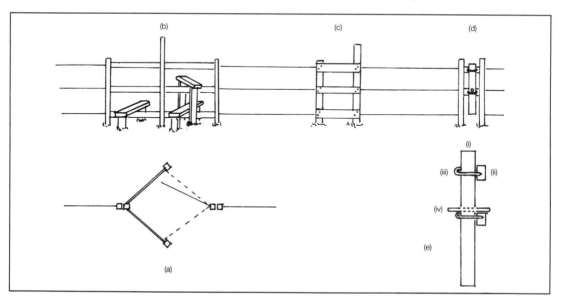

RIGHTS OF WAY ACCESS

(a) Layout for kissing gate
(b) One-step and two-step stiles with handpost
(c) Personal board stile

(d) Dog-gate
(e) Detail of dog-gate
   (i) Gate   (ii) Rail   (iii) U-bolt   (iv) Retaining pin

Rights of way

There are several ways of providing access on public footpaths or bridleways. Kissing gates, for example, are designed to ensure that there is no danger of a gate being left ajar so that livestock find their way out (though sheep might and goats certainly will); hunting gates should be wide enough for horse and rider and should be easy for the rider to open and close them without dismounting. Stiles are the most common type of 'gate' on a public footpath but impossible for those with wheelchairs, and often difficult for the elderly or disabled. The aim is to give the public access where there is a right, and to encourage people to use the stile rather than a gate (which they will no doubt leave open) or clambering over a fence. If the access point on a public right of way is awkward to use, it is more than likely that people will try to find their own way over, under or through your fencing and will weaken or damage it in the process. The land owner, or in some cases the local council, is obliged to maintain a stile so that it is safe to use and it should be as sturdy as the situation merits. It would be wise to check your public liability insurance cover.

If a field is fenced with netting, try to make allowances for responsible people walking their dogs: it is not easy to heave an overweight labrador over a fence or stile but it is quite simple for you to devise a safe self-closing dog-gate which must be opened by the dog's owner rather than giving loose dogs free access. Set two posts close together (just wide enough for a large dog) and put two rails across the gap, with the lower one high enough for a dog to creep under. Drive a U-bolt horizontally into the centre of each rail to take a vertical sliding post which can be raised by the dog's owner to let the animal through. Drive a peg right through the sliding post to prevent it from being lifted completely out of its U-bolts.

The simplest stile for your own use is a single thick board set through the fence at an angle and supported on short driven posts. It is easier to climb if there is a section of wooden rails at that point, built to form part of the stile (but don't create a seesaw by resting the board on a rail) and even easier if it consists of two 'steps' angled across each other. At a point of frequent private access where a gate would be too fiddly, don't just wrap an old fertiliser bag around barbed-wired to protect yourself but set two posts close together and span them with a few boards set on edge as a step ladder — just nail each end flat against the posts.

Badger gates

These are so simple to make through a netting fence and so important to the wellbeing of badgers who have established their runs, probably over several generations. Make a

Simple, top-hinged badger gate set in rabbit-proof fencing: the gate is too heavy for rabbits to push through.

wooden frame at the point where the run crosses the fence line and hang a two-way hinged wire-mesh gate, catflap style, heavy enough to deter rabbits if you wish but light enough for the badgers, who are pretty well built.

Water gates

Water gates are used where a fence line crosses a watercourse, or a ditch which might become a watercourse in a wet season. The aim is to deter livestock from using the course as an escape route but at the same time allow the water through, especially if a stream is in spate and is laden with debris. In general, water gates are designed to dangle and swing (again like catflaps). The hinging device might be loops of chain over a round horizontal pole, or perhaps the horizontal pole itself might rest in crotches so that it can rotate. The gate needs to be heavy enough not to be pushed aside by livestock when the water is low but should be wooden so that it can float and thus rise and fall with the water level. Rigid structures are sometimes made for normally dry gullies but these often trap debris when the gully is flooded after heavy rains and can be forced away by the strength of the water unless carefully designed.

Ditches, culverts and bridges

The subject of field drainage systems is discussed elsewhere; however, ditches typically form part of a boundary and they often need to be crossed at access points in the field. The most common farm bridging system in such situations is based on concrete pipes to carry the ditch's water, setting them on a firm bed and jacketing them with tightly packed soil to a depth of at least 30cm. This jacket should be stonefree and you will then need to backfill over the top in a layer about 15cm deep, then finish off with enough hardcore to give a final build-up of material about 60cm deep above the pipe to protect it from the weight of traffic. In addition, build some kind of headwall at either end to retain the backfill and protect the ends of the pipes. The minimum sensible width of the whole access is 5m for tractors,

allowing vehicles to turn into or out of the access, and as much as 9m for larger equipment. The pipes must be of a large enough diameter not to cause a back-up in the water flow and the minimum recommendation is 23cm for a normal land drainage system serving a catchment area of up to 12ha. On a tight budget, you could perhaps use old oil-drums as pipes, making sure they are thoroughly clean first and setting them in concrete. Whatever you use, set the piping system slightly above the bed of the ditch to avoid silting.

For a small ditch or stream where the heaviest spate would pass through an opening of, say, 0.9m wide by 0.6m high and where there is a good supply of suitable materials to hand, a simple stone bridge could be built. The main problem will be to find wide enough stones to span the top. Cover the span with a deep layer of soil — a 50cm blanket will last a lot longer than one of only 15cm.

The simplest footbridge over any watercourse is a tree trunk, if you can keep your footing! Two or three railway sleepers would be safer, if they are long enough to span the gap. Sleepers and old telephone poles are excellent in theory as supports for a plank bridge, though you should be aware that creosote can cause problems to waterlife, and they are heavy enough to be self-supporting as long as adequate lengths at either end are rested on or imbedded in firm ground. Any wooden footbridge is likely to become slippery with algae and it is worth incorporating battens as treads, or perhaps coconut matting, or a coat of bitumen mixed with grit or coarse sand.

Sleepers can also be used to form the actual surface of the bridge, or use pre-stressed concrete beams butted on to concrete bases or abutments for spans of up to 6m. In principle, a solid wooden beam is not as strong as a truss of lighter material, and this in turn is not as strong as an arch if the span merits it — but once a bridge is large enough for such spans, you are involved with stresses that are best left to a competent engineer.

A lightweight footbridge can be made of concrete sections supported on stone or brick pillars, with a run of galvanised scaffolding tube as a handrail which, if the whole is designed as a gentle arch rather than a straight line, can look more attractive than the materials might suggest. Whatever you use to make a bridge, make quite sure that the gap beneath it is large enough for the watercourse in full spate to flow unimpeded, especially when it is laden with the storm debris — and that, in the case of a stream, can be a huge amount of water in a very short time trying to pound its way through the culvert.

Ha-ha

A ha-ha is a landscaper's deception. It is typically seen on an estate where the occupants of a country house want a clear view of the land beyond the gardens so that it seems to be part of the curtilage but want to keep the gracious herd of grazing Jerseys in the park, not in the garden. The sense of continuity is achieved by building a wall or fence below eye-level, in a ditch sufficiently deep to lower the wall out of sight. The top of the wall or fence will be 20–30cm below eye-level in the ditch.

The ha-ha wall probably needs to be at least 1.2m high to be an effective livestock barrier. Dig a wide, deep ditch along the boundary with a long, gentle slope on its far side to help with the illusion of landscape continuity and to let curious sheep find their way to the bottom of the ditch without giving them a jumping-off point to clear the wall or fence. The slope on the garden side should be more abrupt, but take care that you do not unwittingly form a trap for animals between this slope and the wall. Make sure that the ditch is free-draining so that it is safe for animals: install a drainage system if the lie of the land does not give good natural drainage. If there is likely to be an accumulation of water which might undermine the wall, dig an extra foundation trench for the wall a foot or two deep, backfilled with rubble or broken stones or aggregate packed down firmly, and set the first row of stones on it.

A dry-stone wall can be built against a vertical slope on the garden side of the ditch: its face should incline not less than 15 degrees from the vertical. Top it with capping stones to shed rainwater.

Cattle-grids

Cattle-grids are normally installed in roads or driveways to deter livestock from making use of an opening where the drive crosses a fence line. In essence, a cattle-grid is a shallow pit bridged by metal bars from verge to verge. You will need a bypass gate on either side of the grid for people on foot and also so that livestock can be driven through when necessary. The sides of the grid should be fenced off parallel to the verges.

The pit is as wide as the road (or at least as wide as a vehicle), 25–45cm deep, and as long as necessary to prevent animals from leaping across it — 3m should be ample for livestock and 2.5m might be enough, but remember that you probably need to deter intruding animals as well as confine your own. The concrete floor of the pit should be sloped (say 1 in 50) to drainage holes. The side walls, and intermediate dwarf walls to support the grid where necessary, must be strong enough to take the weight of vehicles, including tractors and lorries: use reinforced concrete, engineering bricks or sleepers. Incorporate a shallow ramp so that small victims like hedgehogs and toads can escape if they fall into the pit.

The railings can be of any steel tubing or rolled steel joists, old railway or tram lines — whatever is handy, flat or round (the latter is possibly more effective). Some people leave them half-bedded so that individual rails can be removed when the pit needs to be cleaned out; others find loose rails much too noisy (a useful burglar alarm!) and either weld all the rails into a single unit or anchor them firmly into the side walls. Set the rails about 12–15cm apart.

III The Farmyard

Hard surfaces

Today the most common hard surfaces on a farm are concrete and hardcore — the latter for roads and the former around buildings. But go back a little: in the 1830s wood, iron and stone were the main paving materials — wood in newly colonised lands (the 'corduroy' roads of North America, for example, made of split tree trunks flat face down), iron for the new railways (and, in an abandoned experiment, for London's street-paving) and stone for the highways. But even then John McAdam, who later lent his name to tarmac, pointed out to the Board of Agriculture: 'It is the native soil which really supports the weight of traffic; while that it is preserved in a dry state, it will carry any weight without sinking, and does in fact carry the road and the carriages also. This native soil must previously be made quite dry, and a covering impenetrable to rain must then be placed over it, to preserve it in that dry state.' His use of tar mixed with graded stone came later; in the meantime the best material to form a road surface with the desired qualities of hardness, smoothness and impenetrability to wet was broken flints, in a layer 20cm deep with a slightly rounded surface to let rain water find its way to the roadside ditches. The crown of the road was not more than 7–12cm high.

The principles still hold good, whatever the surface materials: aim to keep the subsoil dry beneath the road surface, build your road on weedfree, consolidated subsoil, build it so that its crown is proud above the surrounding ground level and with a slight hump to shed the rain into well maintained ditches, and catch hill-water on sloped sites with land drains before it has a chance to reach the road. Lay drains beneath the road, too, if the site is damp. Remove topsoil, but only excavate the subsoil if it is necessary to do so in order to lay an adequate depth of hardcore. Make a really thorough job of compacting the hardcore but leave it proud with a crossfall in the camber, then 'blind' its surface with sand to fill any gaps before laying concrete if used.

A standard farm road width is 2.75m, though you can probably squeeze by with 2.5m unless you expect heavy vehicles. Between buildings, however, you need to take account of the possible width of machinery and the need for good turning circles.

Hardcore is a general term to include a variety of materials laid on subsoil to transmit the traffic load to the ground without being deformed. Typical components are building rubble such as broken bricks and broken concrete, or chalk, crushed limestone, flints, shale, stones and broken rocks (known as scalpings). There should be a mixture of larger and smaller pieces, with as many large ones as possible but also adequate graded smaller particles to fill any gaps. Use larger pieces for the edges of the road, smaller for the middle. Ashes can form part of the hardcore but do avoid clay in it, as it tends to be unstable: even *hoggin*, which is clay-impregnated gravel, should only have a nominal clay content.

Most farm roads need about 15cm of hardcore but 20cm for heavy loads. Under concrete, use at least 15cm of hardcore as a base if the road is used by farm vehicles; elsewhere you might get away with 10–12.5cm as long as the concrete is laid carefully. However, if you expect heavily laden delivery vehicles, you will need reinforced concrete, with mesh laid 3–5cm below the concrete's surface. The minimum thickness of the sub-base under concrete depends on the soil:

with very stable sands and gravels or on the undisturbed foundations of an old road you can often lay concrete direct but on most normal soils you need at least 7.5 cm of sub-base, and twice that depth on weak soils such as peat, silt or heavy clay. The thickness of the concrete itself also depends partly on the soil and partly on the likely weight of traffic. Where the latter is no heavier than, say, a herd of cattle, light tractors and trailers with a maximum axle load of three tonnes, the concrete need be no more than 10 cm thick over normal and very stable soils but 15 cm thick over weak soils. For heavier traffic, increase the depth of the concrete to 12.5–15 cm and 17.5 cm respectively.

Concrete is a combination of cement and aggregates. *Cement* is a powder made by burning limestone and clay at high temperatures: it coalesces when water is added and will bond gravel and sand together, filling air gaps as it does so during a process of chemical reactions which include the emission of heat during hydration (setting) followed by 'curing'. Setting takes 30–60 minutes; after a couple of days the concrete attains a third of its ultimate strength, and two-thirds in a week, but will continue to strengthen for anything from a month to a year. The maximum strength would be obtained from mixing a litre of water with 5 kg cement, but in practice the ratio needs to be a litre to 2 kg before the substance becomes workable, which will give more than half of its potential strength.

Aggregate is a mixture of sand and gravel, ranging from fine sands to pebbles which are usually up to 20 mm across for most purposes. A typical farm concrete mix is the traditional 1:2:4 (by volume, one part cement with two parts sand and four parts coarser aggregate), which is now known as C20P and is used for yards and the floors of livestock housing. C20P is actually 3:5:9 by volume: the proportions by weight are one 50 kg bag of cement, 115 kg of damp sand and 195 kg of coarse aggregate (up to 20 mm).

For roads, yard surfaces, shed floors and so on the size of aggregate can vary from about 12 mm to 40 mm but for precast concrete used to make troughs, fencing posts and blocks the aggregate should not be larger than 20 mm.

Concrete can be bought ready-mixed for volumes of more than $2m^3$ and a standard 'load' is $5m^3$. The alternative is to mix the components yourself, by hand with a shovel for small amounts or in a portable bulk mixer, which can be hired. To mix by hand, put the dry ingredients on a concrete or wooden surface and use the shovel to combine them, then make a little cavity in the heap and add the water very gradually, mixing as you do so by shovelling a little of the dry material from the outer edges of the heap into the cavity, adding more water little by little and mixing well.

Do not lay concrete in frosty or near-freezing weather or in hot weather, and be careful to remove any air pockets as you work. You should try to finish working the concrete before it starts to set and it is best to lay perhaps 5 m at a time, with expansion joints between each section. Concrete will shrink by perhaps 0.5–0.75 per cent while it cures (depending on the proportions of cement and water in the mix) but, more tellingly, it tends to expand in hot weather and then contract again, which could cause cracking. If you are laying concrete in winter, allow for summer expansion by leaving a small gap between each section and filling it with something slightly elastic like softboard impregnated with bitumen. If the joint is likely to impede equipment such as yard scrapers, set the wood a little below surface level and top it up with bitumen.

Tarmac is a mixture of graded stone coated with tar: you would need 5–10 cm of tarmac over well consolidated hardcore, and can finish it with a coating of tar and granite chips.

Yard buildings

Structures

One of the most useful, versatile and simple structures in the yard or in the field is the *pole barn*, which is basically little more than a roof supported by hefty poles but is infinitely adaptable if parts of its sides can be clad. It can be used to house livestock, for example, or for storing straw and hay, as a tractor shed, or a fresh-air milking area. It can be on a scale small enough for a woodshed or big enough for a covered riding school.

The essence of a true pole barn is second-hand materials. Old telegraph poles usually form the main uprights and they are in most cases much longer than needed, which means they can be sunk a long way into the ground so that they are virtually self-supporting under their own weight, with just a small platform of concrete at the feet and the rest of the hole simply backfilled with rammed earth and rubble. The post-hole should be 1.3–1.5 m deep and the concrete base about 20 cm thick and 40 cm square. The poles are braced if necessary and support simple rafters to a monopitch roof.

The barn can be left open-sided, or railed, or clad to give greater security and weather protection for its contents. Most livestock, incidentally, will probably remain healthier in something which is basically a covered yard rather than enclosed in a building: as soon as animals are crowded into a stuffy environment, they become less hardy and disease has every opportunity to flourish and spread. However, they should have at least the option of retreating behind a windbreak under a roof and in the case of goats and young animals separated from their mothers the need for more protection from the weather is greater. In such cases, the sides of the building do need to be clad, but there should also be plenty of fresh air and good ventilation — but not draughts.

A common old building on many holdings is the open-fronted *cartshed*, which is usually walled on three sides under a pitched roof and can be ideal for livstock as well as machinery, as long as it is sensibly sited so that its open face does not receive the brunt of the prevailing wind. Traditional farm buildings often face south east so that they have the benefit of available morning sunlight, especially when the sun is low in the sky in winter, but are shielded from the hot sun of a late summer afternoon.

A typical three-bay shed can be divided by railings or low walls and serve as winter housing for house cows and their calves (with one section being used as a milking parlour if necessary) or a comfortable pigsty, or housing for a small herd of goats or a flock of deep-litter hens. The open face gives ample fresh air and, with luck, sunshine as well, while the depth of a cartshed is usually adequate to allow animals to find shelter at the back when they wish. Even better is an open-fronted shed with direct access to an open-air concrete yard for lounging and exercise.

If a cartshed, pole barn or any other building is being adapted for tractors (either as a tractor shed or as a livestock building which needs to give access to tractors and machinery for daily management) do try to plan ahead and make allowances for the height and width of the machinery. For example, now that so many tractors are

Pigsties converted to confine an active billygoat. *(Anna Oakford).*

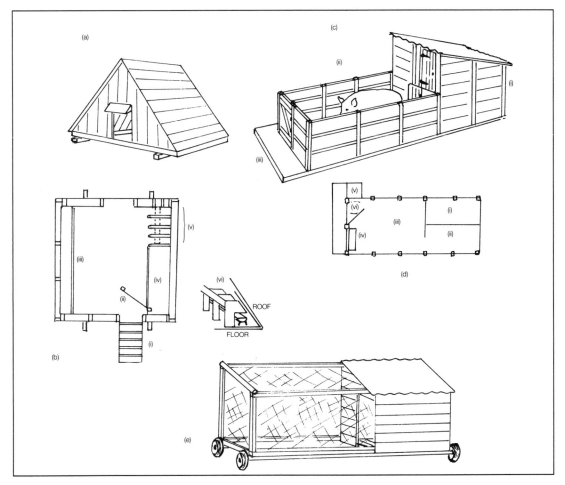

HOUSING FOR SMALL LIVESTOCK

(a) Portable ark for poultry or outdoor pigs

(b) Ark layout for outdoor farrowing hut with double skin for insulation
   (i) Ramp to pig's access door
   (ii) Half-height draught baffle board
   (iii) Floor-level slip rail (note that shape of ark provides safe area for piglets where roof slope meets floor)
   (iv) Piglet nest with creep rail
   (v) Creep with slide-out trough for piglets
   (vi) Detail of (v): trough, partitions, creep rail

(c) Cottager's pigsty, 1945
   (i) Housing 1.4m high at rear, 1.8m at front, with air vent under rear eaves, corrugated roof, two-part door to yard
   (ii) Yard 3.6m × 2.4m, walls 1.1m high of brick or of pre-cast concrete panels supported by pillars at 1.2m intervals
   (iii) Concrete base, including approach to yard gate, insulated under housing

(d) Cottager's pigsty: layout
   (i) Bed area, raised 7–8cm above pen
   (ii) Pen, raised 5cm above yard
   (iii) Yard
   (iv) Trough, half-round glazed drainpipe or galvanised
   (v) Drainage sump, preferably with bucket for instant removal of effluent
   (vi) Gate into yard

(e) Home-made portable fold unit for a goat, with shelter and netted run

101

Solidly built yard for weaners — simple and strong. *(Anna Oakford)*.

fitted with safety cabs, extra height is needed at building entrances and this rather obvious fact is sometimes overlooked in the planning stages of conversion or new building.

The illustrations give ideas about structures for housing livestock on a small scale within a modest farmyard. The fun of farming lies in exercising your ingenuity and adapting to circumstances: each holding is very individual (thank heavens!) and any suggestions given can only be for guidance — don't consider them to be rules! However, your top priority with livestock must always be the welfare of the animal and with this in mind you should usually provide too much space rather than too little. You should also try to plan the buildings to suit the animal that has to live in them rather than designing for your personal convenience. Please.

Here is a small tip for the do-it-yourself builder. When marking out the site of a new building, it is essential to lay down accurate right angles at corners. Make yourself a 'set square' in the form of a triangular wooden frame. If the three sides of the triangle are in the proportions 3:4:5, you will have a true right angle. To be sure that the walls really will be square to each other, measure the diagonals of the site lines: they should be equal to each other in length in a simple rectangle or square if all four corners are 90 degrees.

There are several points to consider if you are investing in new buildings and particular attention should be paid to their effect in the landscape from a distance, as well as more closely. Take a look at the Buildings and Landscape Table:

Buildings and Landscape

POINTS TO CONSIDER

Consider the effect of the proposed building from a distance.

★ ISOLATED buildings are more obtrusive than those which are part of a group. Put isolated buildings into natural land folds rather than against the skyline.

★ PITCHED ROOFS are often conspicuous: they reflect more light than vertical surfaces. Steeper pitches blend better with hilly landscapes, more level ones with flat and rolling landscapes. On a slope, step the roof levels, and anyway excavate into the slope rather than building out from it: try to keep the contours more intact from the distance. Two roofs might appear less dominant than one large one.

★ BULK can be less obtrusive if the surface is broken — use space boarding, or horizontal bands of different materials. Use more extensive overhangs to cast shadows and give shape to an overwhelming slab of building, also doors/windows to break up the surface.

★ COLOUR is very important: the soft light of northern latitudes intensifies colours (hot Mediterranean sun tones them down). Traditional British country-side colours are earth tones — reds, ochres, browns; also black-and-white, which remains cheerful in dull weather. Be careful with greens — they easily clash with natural vegetation colours, especially bright apple greens. Warm greys can be good in the landscape, but often clash with each other: use a very different grey or another colour altogether in contrast. Light colours make buildings seem larger and more conspicuous; dark ones have the opposite effect: on a large rural building have the roof darker than the walls. Blend colours of new buildings with those of existing structures as well as with landscapes.

★ The Design Council publishes a booklet on *Colour Finishes for Farm Buildings*. Advice is also obtainable from the Farm Buildings Information Centre set up by the Farm Buildings Association and the Royal Agricultural Society of England at the National Agricultural Centre, Stoneleigh, Kenilworth, Warwickshire CV8 2LG (telephone 0203 22345).

Materials

The following are suggestions rather than absolutes. Most farmers, on whatever scale, are adept at using whatever materials come to hand, and it does not necessarily follow that the most expensive buildings are the best. For livestock, bear in mind that the major factors ، are the animal's comfort (psychological as well as physical) and the need for a high standard of hygiene. To both these ends, the building should be as easy to manage as you can make it because a miserable animal handler makes for a miserable animal. So, basically, the materials used (and the way they are put together) should be such that the structure is easy to keep thoroughly clean, especially between batches of animals, and has a dry floor, which means sensible drainage and a hard surface under any bedding.

Floors

Starting with basics, old buildings might have nothing more sophisticated than earth floors. If the foundation is of chalk or sandy soil, then the natural drainage might be good enough, but clay is rammed and must then be drained as if it is concrete. Hardcore also needs to be well rammed to make quite sure that loose stones do not cause foot problems. On top of these materials most people add a base layer of flint-free chalk, ground limestone, power-station fly ash, deep sand (non-abrasive type), or perhaps thick mats of bundled brushwood (faggots), old wattle hurdles or straw bales (with strings removed) to act as a sort of underlay for the bedding, giving much needed insulation from ground-damp and cold.

Basic earthen floors are not easy to keep clean and a few buildings have wooden floors, which are warm but are also difficult to keep clean. Old stone or brick floors have too many nooks and crannies for harbouring disease-carrying organisms and most buildings today have concrete floors, which are easy to clean and drain and are also tight enough to be vermin-proof.

Bedding

Bedding materials for housed livestock provide warmth and comfort and also traditionally absorb manure, though many modern systems (especially intensive ones) give the animals nothing more comfortable than concrete or slatted floors as a bed, sometimes with the benefit of matting. Don't do it! The main bedding materials are straw, sawdust, wood-chips, peat, shredded newspaper or sand. Wheat straw is better than barley as the latter tends to be eaten; sawdust must be from a reliable source and contain no harmful chemicals — you could also use by-products such as wood fibre or bark; peat needs to be quite deep and its main drawbacks are that it makes the place look so dark and that we are beginning to run out of this non-renewable natural material. Sawdust, peat and sand in particular need to be on a good drainage layer.

Walls and rooves

Here again, the choice of materials is a wide one and depends on taste, local availability and finances. The obvious walling materials are timber, brick, stone, concrete and all kinds of fabricated sheeting, corrugated or plain — galvanised steel, fibre cement, aluminium, and plastics of many kinds (rigid or flexible), many of which can also be used for roofing. But improvise! Use secondhand materials like sleepers (if you can find them) or try your hand with brushwood, hurdles, wattle-and-daub, adobe (sun-baked bricks made of clayey or loamy soil) or straw. On a small scale and a tight budget, these are genuine options if you are prepared to invest a little time and ingenuity. They might not last for ever, but their disposability ensures good hygiene and they are all natural materials which will cause no disposal problems.

Building with straw

In 1945 the Ministry of Agriculture, acutely aware of the shortage of building materials and skilled labour in a war-weary country, encouraged the use of straw for farm storage and stockyards. Straw has many advantages as a building material: it provides very good insulation; it can be cheap if locally available; and can simply be replaced before it becomes unhygienic. The illustrations give some ideas for using straw, either in bales or as thatch, ranging from huge poultry enterprises and large straw yards for cattle to traditional lambing yards and simple field shelters for calves or pigs. All you need, apart from the straw, are some rough poles and stakes and perhaps some wire netting.

The best building straw is probably wheat, though any kind of straw can be used, including bean straw. It can be in bales, or loose between two layers of wire netting, or can be formed into mats. The main problems with straw are fire and possible pests such as fungi and fleas. It is important that the site is adequately drained, to prevent the straw becoming waterlogged.

Strawbales are ideal for creating calf or lamb *igloos* within a building. Very young calves are 'lying up' animals, like very young deer: their natural preference is to lie quietly in long grass or shrubbery for many hours at a time, alone, while the mother grazes with the herd, usually nowhere near the youngster, but returns to suckle now and then. In the wild, therefore, these young animals are used to isolation in their first few days of life and appreciate a hideaway where they feel out of sight and safe. A straw igloo of bales fits the bill nicely, giving them a sense of safety and also protecting them from draughts. Simply set up a pen of bales within a loose box, and make it even more snug with a makeshift roof if you wish.

A slightly more elaborate *bale shelter* can be built in a field for youngstock of all kinds or for poultry, but if older animals are also in the field the bales will need extra support and protection or they will be pushed over, rubbed to pieces and eaten. Stack the bales bondwise like bricks to a height appropriate to the youngstock, and use perhaps an old door or some corrugated sheeting for a roof. Chicken netting helps to protect the structure from being pulled to pieces, and a few poles and rails will give it more stability against butting and scratching. The less the weight of the straw, the greater the need for support. Be a little wary of goats: they are

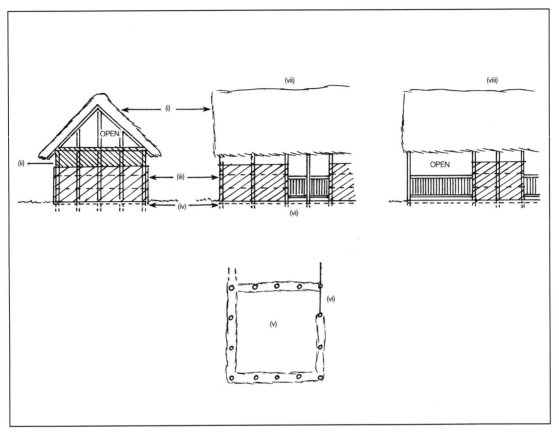

STRAW BUILDINGS

(a) For pigs

   (i) Straw thatch roof over sheep netting
  (ii) Chickenwire panels, 0.75m high, stuffed with loose straw, on ends of building but not on sides
 (iii) Pig-netting panels 1.5m high, stuffed with straw, or straw-bale walls
 (iv) Horizontal line of barbed-wire to prevent rooting
  (v) Floor plan showing larchpole uprights (15–20cm in diameter) with netting stapled to inside and outside faces for packing with straw. Width of house 3.65m; length 3.65m with option to extend
 (vi) Gate of 7.5cm slats, 7.5cm apart
 (vii) Sow house based on (v)
(viii) Rearing house with partly slatted walls (0.8m high)

born mountaineers and will delightedly spend as much time on top of their shelter as within it if they think the roof is accessible.

A very *temporary shelter* can be made with a few poles supporting a roof. Pile loose straw over the top and against side rails: it will be snug but has only a short life as it will soon become wet through. It would be better to use loose straw as thatch for the sides as well as the roof: set some upright poles about 20cm apart for the walls and weave wisps of straw among them like wattling, beating down these horizontal courses as you work to make the walls draughtproof and weaving in a split rod (hazel or willow, for example) every metre or so to keep the uprights in place. If you sprinkle the inside face with mud, the straw is less likely to be eaten.

To finish, a *straw door* or shutter could be made as well: make a framework of rods bound together with wire and braced with crosspieces, ensuring that one of the two uprights is strong enough to act as a hanging warp, then wind a straw rope, up to 5cm thick, from top to bottom as the weft, and a more tightly drawn straw rope woven horizontally among them like a mat. You could make a double panel, weaving separately on each side side of the frame (the basis of an old-fashioned straw mattress, which would have the gap stuffed with loose straw). To make a *straw rope*: attach a stout wire hook to a large whimbrel and twist a loop of dampened straw into the hook (sprinkle it with water the night before). Walk backwards slowly, twisting the straw into a rope and feeding in fresh straw as it lengthens. When it is complete, fasten it at either end to fence posts or trees to let it dry so that it will not unwind when released.

For a temporary *thatched shelter*, designed to last perhaps 12–15 years if it is out of reach of hungry livestock, you need a very steep pitch to the roof to help the thatch shed water. On a building 6m wide, for example, the ridge pole should be 3m higher than the eaves. Cut rafters of 5cm softwood poles long enough to project by 30cm. Nail on 2.5cm lathes 20–25cm apart. Compact a bunch of straw with your hands and tie this bundle to the lowest two poles so that its butt projects to form the eaves. Lay a complete row of similar bundles along the front, tying them firmly to stop the wind lifting them. Then lay and tie a second row: let their butts come down even with the first but only tie them to the third pole. Lay and tie a third row so that the butts come about 23cm above those of the first two and then continue in this fashion as if laying shingles. To finish off, bind ample straw across the comb, running a wire or two along each side and 'stitching' with wire (you need a helper under the roof to feed the stitching wire back through the straw to you). The actual bunches can be tied in place with twine or willow ties.

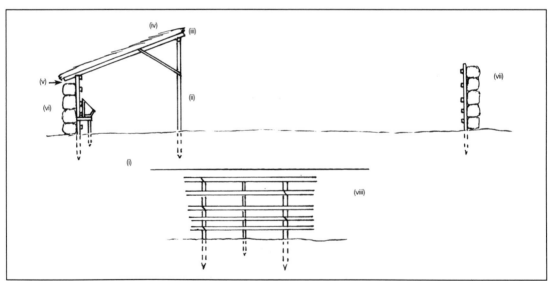

(b) Straw yard for cattle, 20m × 20m, with straw-bale walls

- (i) Covered area running full length of back wall
- (ii) 4.3m roof-support larch poles at 3m apart, braced by sycamore rails from front to back
- (iii) Split ash rafters, 0.4m apart
- (iv) Straw thatch over layer of thorn or brushwood
- (v) Ventilation gap between roof and back wall
- (vi) Straw bales (four high, placed lengthways) forming back wall against yard fence
- (vii) Straw bales (five high, placed lengthways) forming front wall against yard fence, broken by 3m gateway
- (viii) Detail of yard fence supporting and protecting bales: can be 3, 4 or 5 rails; posts 3m long (2.1 above ground) and 3m apart, with stud post between

In *straw yards* for cattle, shelter is provided by complete walls of bales, or by pitching up straw stacks on three sides of the yard with rails on the fourth side. Ten bullocks would need a yard about 9m × 14m (internal measurements), with its south side consisting of rails, gates and a drinking trough and the other three walls about a metre thick. Four courses of bales, making walls about 2.5m high, would need perhaps 7t of straw. The walls can be protected with wire netting or chestnut paling, or a coating of creosote, or an internal post-and-rail fence set about 1.5m into the yard to form a feeding channel between fence and walls. The walls could also be of loose straw stuffed between horizontal wires or wire netting, supported by pairs of poles each 2m apart and perhaps 3m tall above ground level. The higher the walls of a straw yard, the less need there is for a roof.

The old shepherds made great use of straw to provide their ewes with warm, sheltered *lambing yards* or folds: they used straw hurdles or brushwood faggots to form windbreaks and set up lambing pens made from wattle hurdles for sides, back and top, the roof being a straw-thatched hurdle. One of the great advantages of these typical downland folds was that fresh sites could be used and any build-up disease could be avoided.

Field shelters

Simple shelters are much appreciated by livestock in the field: they offer respite from wind-driven rain and from summer flies. They can double up as confinement for a couple of animals when necessary — for example to keep a house cow's calf away from the udder but still in company with its mother, or to hold a cow temporarily for the attention of a vet or AI operative, or to provide a protected 'creep' for younger animals.

Traditional South Downs lambing fold snugly protected by wattles and thatch, with hurdles (upside down!) to confine each ewe with her lambs.

'Rustic' field shelter for house cow and calf, made very cheaply from secondhand materials.

Strawbale field shelters are useful but temporary and often not strong enough to confine an animal who would rather be elsewhere. More permanent shelters can be built from whatever secondhand materials can be found. Above is an example of a field shelter salvaged from long-derelict woodland cottages with sleepers providing a self-supporting foundation for hefty old window-frames forming the wall framework, clad with wany-elm boards (the top two of which make a removable shutter); cottage doorpost, joists and rafters become corner posts, larch poles support corrugated-iron roofing sheets, and Christmas tree thinnings or smaller larch poles make the calf-proof front railings and gate. Later, broken paving slabs from the local council made a dry floor inside and also under the substantial roof overhang which was designed partly to keep the weather out and also to offer shade and a dry back to the cow when her calf was confined to the shed. This small shelter (3 m × 2.5 m) was used for several years by two house cows and their calves, serving as field shelter, calf house and milking parlour, and it cost almost nothing except time and labour. It continued to stand when the cows were replaced by horses, until equine teeth gradually eroded the uprights at the base, beaver-fashion.

Field shelters for smaller livestock such as sheep and goats can be even simpler: a half-hoop of corrugated iron forming roof and back, perhaps, with a slatted floor if possible, makes a structure light enough to be transported to a new site as soon as its surroundings become poached. Remember, as already warned, that goats will treat a low shelter like a crag and its top needs to be tough enough to take the pressure of dancing feet.

Outdoor pigs, too, are happy enough with a simple half-hoop of corrugated forming a small-scale Nissen hut, or a portable ark like those used for chickens but more substantial. A better design for outdoor pigs is the 'pigloo', which has an entrance designed to baffle the wind. A substantial field house for pigs could be made of straw bales, roofed with loose straw over a wooden framework, and perhaps with a yard enclosed by corrugated metal sheets attached to driven stakes. The essence of pig accommodation is a dry, draught-free sleeping compartment with an unroofed exercise and feeding yard. As pigs have always been cottagers' animals, there is a long history of ingenuity in designing and building cheap homemade sties using salvaged materials.

Pigs, of course, enjoy wallowing and will be delighted to have access to a boggy corner somewhere on their range. In contrast, poultry prefer a dustbath and need a permanently dry patch of earth for the purpose.

These contrasting essentials to grooming should always be made available.

Polypens

The newest simple field housing for smaller livestock is the polypen, which is effectively an overgrown polythene plant tunnel. The system is particularly useful for poultry, or a herd of fibre goats or a small flock of sheep and is ideal for lambing. The sides are clad with strengthened materials but are not robust enough for cattle.

Creeps

A creep is an area accessible only to youngsters and not to older animals in the same environment; it is an area where the little ones can feed or shelter in peace. The simplest creep is a fencing barrier low or narrow enough for only smaller animals to pass through. It might give them access to a whole area of fresh grazing, or to their own little shelter or yard, or to a feeding point,

Polypen housing for a flock of grading-up Angora goats and kids.

either in the field or within housing. The barrier must be strong enough to resist older animals, of course, and in a long run of fencing there should be a series of creeps at no more than 50m intervals.

Fold units

Fold units are designed to be more or less portable, so that an animal can be restricted to a small area of grazing and then moved to a fresh area daily or as often as necessary. They are widely used for poultry and can also be adapted for goats and pigs where the option is preferred to tethering. Some are wheeled for transport but most have to be lifted, either by two people or with the aid of a tractor. Most combine housing with a run and there are many designs on the market for different purposes but many people prefer to build their own. The secret is to strike a balance between portability and sturdiness.

Pens

Pens and runs might be intended as permanent features but more often they need a degree of portability to avoid an area becoming stale and building up a wormload and disease. They are commonly used for all kinds of poultry and rabbits but, like folds, can also be adapted for goats, pigs and sheep or young calves. Sometimes they are little more than confined spaces on grass or earth, or they can incorporate simple housing. Electric fencing can be used but most runs and pens rely on wire netting.

The mesh size needs to be appropriate not only to the stock being confined but also to likely intruders such as predators and rodents. For a permanent pen, the netting should be buried at the foot, turning in a horizontal plane to deter digging. If you are confining rabbits, for example, the buried section is directed inwards, but if your concern is predatory foxes, turn the netting outwards. It might also be necessary to turn the netting at its top, usually at an angle of about 45 degrees, to deter climbers into or out of the pen, and against intruders it might help to add a couple of strands of barbed wire there as well. If foxes are a problem, set an electrified scare wire at nose level (see Fencing).

If a pen is an aviary with a roof, the roofing can be of much lighter mesh but watch out for the weight of snow pressing it down. Snow also raises the ground level, so make sure your pen walls will still be high enough!

Farmyard drainage

The major problem with farmyard drainage, even on a small scale, is the safe disposal of pollutants, particularly from livestock manure, silage effluent, agrochemicals and detergents. In 1990 even stronger regulations were introduced to tackle the increasing risk to the country's watercourses from such yard effluents, especially stored silage and slurry.

Your local water authority will be prepared — indeed eager — to give helpful advice on avoiding pollution problems and you will in any case need the authority's approval for drainage schemes and its information on current legislation. The new rules are tough, as they must be.

Slurry

Slurry is stored temporarily in pits, tanks, silos or compounds, the designing of which depends on the volume of slurry, the permeability of the soil, the height of the water table, proximity to watercourses, site features, costs and stringent regulations. The water authority will give advice according to individual circumstances on slurry storage and the spreading of slurry on the land.

Quite apart from its potential as a powerful pollutant, slurry is dangerous in another way. Animals, children, adults and tractors can drown in slurry and any type of slurry store should be adequately fenced to protect the unwary. Like an iced pond, slurry tends to form a deceptively solid crust on top but remains lethally liquid below. Slurry lagoons are particularly dangerous: they are designed for the permanent storage of unwanted effluent and are either large open ponds or extensive ditches. They have a substantial surface area and act rather like enormous septic tanks, allowing bacteria to break down waste material and containing the waste while allowing the resulting clean water to escape. They were unwittingly predicted on a huge scale in Richard Jefferies' unnerving and almost sci-fi book, *After London, or Wild England*, written more than a century ago. Read it!

Yard water

Apart from manure, slurry and silage, the effluents from a typical farmyard include large quantities of water which has been used for sluicing down floors in livestock systems (housing, milking parlours and so on) and rainwater run-off from rooves or hard yard surfaces. Again, consult the local water authority to ensure that potential pollutants are safely channelled and do not inadvertently enter the water courses by means of ditches. Rainwater can be disposed of directly into watercourses or by simple soakaways (underground 'reservoirs' of rubble or gravel) if the subsoil is suitable but contaminated water needs separate drainage and disposal systems.

Gutters, downpipes, gullies, drains and chambers should ideally be designed to accept maximum stormwater. It used to be suggested that the maximum allowance should be 25 mm per hour but more recently a safer allowance for rainstorms of up to 75 mm per hour has become more common. They used to say that downpours of such an intensity only occurred for five minutes every four years or for twenty minutes every fifty years in the UK but times seem to be a-changing . . .

Roof run-off can be stored and used for small scale irrigation, for washing down yards and parlours, for diluting slurry or reserved for fire-fighting but it should be stored quite separately from foul drainage. There is no harm in a few good old-fashioned water butts about the place and indeed they can be invaluable in times of drought.

In the drainage of a farmyard, as opposed to an ordinary domestic property, certain special factors need to be taken into account:

★ Avoid (or protect) downpipes on the corners of buildings: they will be damaged by livestock, lorries, tractors and machinery.
★ Install 'stableyard' or bucket drain-inlets if straw or other waste is likely to be washed into the drains; and have manholes for easy access to clean them out.
★ Make sure that hard surfaces have adequate and regular falls towards the gullies (1 in 50, say) and set the gullies in the middle of hardstanding. Use open channels where the fall is inadequate for pipes.
★ Have straight drain runs for easy cleaning and install manholes or inspection chambers at junctions.
★ If a large drain joins a smaller one, have the *top* of the pipes level rather than the bottom.
★ Watch out for flooding into areas which are below ground level.
★ Protect all drainage and plumbing systems from damage by livestock. And — just a passing thought — bear in mind that some cows spook at a line painted on concrete across their path, and might refuse to trust a drainage channel.

Plumbing

Your water authority will be happy to advise on suitable pipe sizes for any application but here are some basic facts. Mains water is under pressure, and its pressure or 'head' is measured in pounds force per square inch (psi) or feet (the height of an equivalent column of water: 1 psi = 2.3 ft). In the metric system, 1 kg force per square centimetre (1 kgf/cm^2) is the equivalent of a 10 m head. Distribution pressure is supplied by pumping, or by storage at a high level in a cistern or water tower.

Cold-water supply pipes are usually of polythene or PVC. Polythene is lightweight, flexible, easy to lay underground and simple to join; PVC is rigid and its joints have to be welded with solvent. Hot-water pipes are usually of copper or galvanised steel. In the milking parlour there are also pipes and fittings of rubber, glass and stainless steel.

The imperial pipe bores were measured in fractions of an inch by quarter-inch increments between half an inch and two inches. Metric measurements fall into four classes, the most common of which is Class C (90 m head, 9 kgf/cm^2).

Pipes for field installations are usually 150 mm mains with 100 mm laterals, with underground valves and take-off points. Do remember to mark (permanently and visibly) the location of such points: manholes soon get covered by growth and soil and can take a lot of unearthing in an emergency. And remember where you keep the stopcock handle — your arm never seems to be long enough to reach down to the tap, nor your hand small enough to work inside the chamber. Finally, spare a thought for small creatures which might get trapped in an uncovered chamber: even hedgehogs have managed to find their way down an open vertical pipe and got stuck.

Pipe systems to feed out-of-door outlets such as field water troughs need to be buried about 80 cm below ground level to be safe from frost and the pressure of heavy vehicles. If in doubt about the frost depth, insulate, whether indoors or outside; and also keep the water moving. One of the worst winter jobs is trying to break the morning ice on a field trough or to defrost a standpipe before it bursts. A tip for your cows' water trough outside: insulate the up-pipe with a jacket of nice, warm manure or plenty of well protected straw.

Livestock drinking troughs must above all supply fresh drinking water and need to be checked at least daily for leaks, overflows, freezing and ballcock failures. Protect the ballcock from inquisitive and playful animals, for a start: the area around a tank quickly becomes a mudbath from overflows. Provide raised stands for smaller animals such as lambs — something hefty which will not be dislodged, like old railway sleepers, though I have seen them float away on a flood. Also consider barn owls, who seem to have a fascination for their reflections in field water troughs and have been known to drown themselves because of the lack of a means of clambering out.

Tanks are usually of galvanised steel or concrete. If you make do with an old bath, ensure that the plug has not perished and that the overflow has an appropriate outlet to take excess water well away from the area. If you rely on a hose rather than the mains, what are you going to do about freezing in winter?

A tank 45 cm wide and 40 cm deep would have a capacity of 50 litres for every 30 cm of its length, and a cattle trough of these dimensions 1.8 m long might be adequate for 30 cows. Think not only about capacity but also habits: cattle tend to drink communally, for example, and you should make sure that even the lowest in the bunting order has access to water. The daily requirements of livestock vary enormously according to individual temperament, age, size, time of year and whether or not the animal is being milked or suckled. The aim should be to ensure that no animal ever thirsts or has to resort to stale, warm or contaminated water.

IV   Livestock

There is an increasing problem in this country which is only now beginning to be appreciated. More and more of those who buy land do not have adequate experience of livestock and have to buy the experience of others. For example, many newcomers choose sheep as what they believe might be the easy option for keeping the grass down, whether in a small paddock or on a family farm, but sheep are not 'easy-care' animals: they need dipping, for example, and they need shearing. Very few new sheep owners are competent to shear their own flocks and they therefore look to shearing contractors who, in turn, are so overwhelmed by the demand for their services that they rely on teams of New Zealanders and Australians. The waiting lists grow longer and that sometimes results in incompetent shearing either by 'cowboys' or by small-flock owners no longer willing to wait. The sheep suffer.

It is beyond the scope of this book to deal with stockmanship, a subject of considerable depth which owes more to experience and 'feel' or empathy than to received knowledge. The aim of this section is to explain, briefly, the basic choices of types of livestock and systems for various situations, to discuss animal behaviour in the context of handling, and to give techniques for routine procedures. It does not include, for example, nutrition, diseases, breeding, or the processing or marketing of animal produce.

Choices

There are types of livestock and types of enterprise for every conceivable situation and it is a matter of choosing the right species or combination of species and the appropriate management aims and systems to meet the circumstances. The first golden rule is: choose the right animal for the existing environment rather than trying to alter an environment for an inappropriate animal.

Breeds have been created over many generations for specific purposes, essentially to thrive in certain regional environments and also to meet certain production requirements such as the provision of meat, milk, fibre or muscle power, or alternatively (and usually at the same time) a pleasing or remarkable appearance by way of, say, coat colour, wool type or shape and length of horn. In general, it makes sense to use a local breed, or a breed commonly used locally which has proved suitable to the area's climate and soil.

Management systems for different types of livestock also offer a wide choice. The first is one of degree, ranging between the extremes of intensive and extensive farming.

Intensive farming depends on a high level of inputs to achieve a high level of outputs. Such systems cut back on the amount of land per head of livestock, often by confining the animals indoors and buying in their food, but thereby increase the risk of disease and the labour in feeding and mucking out, unless they are mechanised. Mechanisation, of course, serves to widen the gap between human and animal so that the livestock become numbers rather than individuals, with all the drawbacks of such anonymity.

It is said that housing is to the benefit of the stock but too often it is more to the benefit of the stockman (who can keep in the dry, for a start) and the animals are subjected to the inevitable physical and psychological stresses of confinement and high productivity so that standards of stockmanship need to be very high — and sometimes are not. Because the animal is unable to counterbalance environmental adversity by moving away from it, the costs of environmental control, veterinary fees and feed-company bills are substantial but are offset by the high returns. Extreme examples of intensive farming include battery systems for egglayers or broilers, indoor pig-keeping, and in south west USA in particular 'dirt lot' beef systems in which the animals are crowded together in huge bare-earth compounds with no grazing at all and fed with concentrates and cut-and-carry fodder.

Extensive farming is the very opposite in its extremes. The animals range freely over comparatively large areas of poorer land, for example hill-farm sheep flocks and suckler herds. They receive little in the way of supplementary feeding, and they need only the most basic shelter. That is not to say the stock and land are not actively managed — indeed the need for skilled stockmanship and fieldcraft is increased — but overheads and capital costs are low, corresponding with lower production expectations, and there is quite a strong case to be made for the psychological benefits. In contrast to extreme intensive systems, extensive farming allows animals to express a wide range of natural behaviour patterns and activities and, while they might experience the physical discomforts of the climate, they have the option to take evasive measures and tend to be much hardier and less susceptible to the diseases that are so often prevalent among confined livestock — assuming, as already suggested, that they are of a breed appropriate to the system.

Between the extremes there are the typical situations of many good smallholdings — for example, the small free-ranging poultry flock which is housed at night but allowed to scratch about in orchard and yard by day, or the meadow housecows with access to a sound field shelter and a winter cowshed, or the paddock sheep flock, or the handful of pigs rooting the potential kitchen garden. If you want to keep outdoor pigs on a slightly larger scale, your holding should be on light, well drained soil (sands, gravels or chalk) in an area with an annual rainfall of less than 750mm, and you should ensure the pigs have access to shade and wallows in summer and to optional hard standing in winter.

It is not only in the degree of confinement that intensive and extensive systems differ but also the number of animals per unit of land or floor area. Stocking rates for outdoor systems cannot be laid down on tablets of stone: they depend upon too many environmental variables such as the adequacy of the grazing, the land's susceptibility to poaching, or extremes of climate, and human variables such as available manpower (or perhaps dogpower), means of access to outlying areas (on foot, in the saddle, or by bike, all-terrain vehicle or tractor) and the requirements for production levels and regularity. In intensive systems, the stocking rates are dense.

In general, the lower the stocking rate, the more each animal can gain from and return to the land, and the more likely it is that each animal will be regarded as an individual rather than an anonymous numbered unit.

Animal behaviour

An understanding of animal behaviour is essential for those who intend to care for livestock of any kind. Good stock sense is partly innate but is obviously improved with experience, especially if you make a deliberate point of gate-leaning, simply observing your stock in the field for long periods so that your presence among them is ignored and you can see how they behave left to their own devices. (A field easily in view of the house is a bonus.) *Always* make time for regular contemplations like this, however many years you have been at it and however large or small your herd or flock. On the very best of the large commercial dairy farms, for example, at least half an hour twice a day is set aside for 'just looking' and, like a writer taking a walk to untangle the plot of a novel, this apparent skiving or idling in fact plays an important part in good management. As Richard Jefferies described it in *The Toilers of the Field*: 'The agricultural labourers, both men and women, are a slow set, never in a hurry; there is none of that bustle characteristic of the town people, even of the lowest classes. They take every opportunity of leaning on the prong-handle, or standing in the shade — they seem to have no idea of time.'

It also pays to observe other people's animals, for years if necessary, before taking on the responsibility of your own stock. If you have half a chance to offer casual labour on a stock farm, seize it, or consider part-time work as, say, a Milk Marketing Board recorder or a pig inseminator as a good excuse to observe a number of differently managed enterprises.

Never despise the saws of apparently out-of-date old stockmen: they have learned a great deal more from a lifetime of observation and experience, often enhanced by the experience of their predecessors, than any college-educated farm manager, university graduate or scientist. Smallholders are often more stockwise than large-scale stock farmers in that they identify their animals as individuals and get to know their ways well, very often knowing them from birth to table, literally.

The study of behaviour in farm animals is not just part of an emotional bond with them: it is thoroughly practical. If you know how and why a particular individual behaves normally, then you will quickly detect any change in its behaviour, however slight and indefinable, that might be an early indication of illness or will tell you that a cow is ready for the bull or a ewe is thinking of lambing. It is all too easy for commercial farmers, and scientific animal behaviourists, to overlook the fact that animals *are* individuals: they share a broad pattern of behaviour, just like human beings do, but there are as many differences between them as similarities.

The childhood rhyme, 'What is this world if, full of care/We have no time to stand and stare,' is the good stockman's creed, not the idler's excuse. And if you cannot have your stock close to home so that you can see them as you glance from the window — or, worse, if you are habitually absent from the holding during the day (in which case, should you really have livestock at all?) — then for heaven's sake make sure that you or a reliable ally visit them regularly, at the very least twice a day even if the animals do not need supplementary feeding, and when you get there, stay there and stare.

Handling

A good handler understands the animals and tries to exploit their natural behaviour rather than work in conflict with their instincts. Nearly all our domesticated farm animals are herd creatures and that makes it easier to move groups but much more difficult to separate individuals from their group. Bear in mind that to separate or, worse, completely isolate an individual from its group can inflict considerable psychological stress on the animal and your aim should always be to minimise distress — if not for the sake of the animal, then for the sake of its productivity, which will be reduced under stress.

All herbivores are alert to predation, and they have eyes set so that they have good peripheral vision: they can catch a glimpse of an approach at a wide angle, and this can make them spook at shadowy or fluttery movements to the side. They are always suspicious of the unusual and will immediately sense your intentions if you want to move them, handle them, load them or whatever, however benevolent your aims. Once they are on guard, your problems begin! That is one of the reasons for practising regular handling in harmless circumstances. If you only catch up an animal when you want to do something unpleasant to it, don't be surprised if it regards your every approach with extreme distrust. And do make use of food as a lure, even if it does teach them bad habits like shouting hopefully to every passing stranger.

One of the easiest tricks in the book, whether you are trying to house a farm animal, catch a runaway pet or trap a pest, is to lull them into a sense of security by feeding at a point to which they must gain access through some form of channelling and get them used to passing through it so that, when the day of reckoning comes, they enter the 'trap' willingly. For example, loading into a vehicle is nearly always a problem whether you are taking animals back to the yard or to a show or to the abattoir, but if they are allowed to become familiar with the loading ramp and the vehicle and learn to associate it with food the whole process on the day will be much easier. Ramps can be a major problem: most animals are wary of a surface which sounds insecurely 'hollow' underfoot, or gives them an uncertain footing, or presents a rather sudden slope. The more gentle the incline and the better its surface grip, the more readily will they accept it. The section on Handling Facilities explains the importance of being properly equipped for different handling situations and making use of races and funneling systems.

Training for occasional handling is well worthwhile if you have only a few animals. Accustom a young one to a halter right from the start and take it for regular walks, at an age before it realises that it might be strong enough to take *you* for a walk, be it a bull calf, a lamb, a kid or a foal. Piglets need harnesses: they are quite the wrong shape for halters. Very early training to halter or harness is also invaluable if you intend to tether-graze.

Carrying

Most smaller animals (including calves) should be carried with one arm around the chest and the other around the rump, so that the animal's legs dangle. Do not take the animal's weight with an arm encircling its middle, as you will certainly cause discomfort and could even damage internal organs. Poultry can be carried on or under one arm, head to the rear, with your hand under the body holding the legs gently if the bird is restless.

Cattle

Cows are herd animals, with a definite social hierarchy, and are much happier if they are allowed to remain in their own social group where each knows her place. They are creatures of habit and deliberation, and they respond much better to kind, quiet treatment than to brute force and shouting. It is said that the ideal cow-handler is a self-confident introvert. Don't lose your temper, don't chase around the place, don't be tentative or unpredictable. Whenever possible, maintain regular routines. Let cows come to you: stand still, or walk away slowly, and very often their curiosity will get the better of them. Rather than driving them as if you were a cowboy, call them up or lure them (the rattle of food in a bucket is useful). Never hurry cows: they like to move at their own pace, with dignity, and any attempt to speed them up will unsettle them and make them much more awkward and perverse.

If an individual fails to be persuaded to enter a confined space by lures or sheer guile, there are one or two last-resort methods of moving it but only when gentle tactics have compeltely failed and you are at an impasse in spite of having taken a break for the animal to regain its composure. Work from behind: either pass a rope (or link arms with someone else) against the animal's rump and heave it forward or carefully hold the tail about halfway down and begin to coil it in a flat circle against the rump to put pressure on the tail root, or simply pinch the base of the tail. (If you want a fidgety cow to keep still, hold the tail closer to its root than to its tassel and raise it almost vertically — this will also stop a kicker.)

Alternatively, but preferably not, grip it by the lower jaw (especially a calf) or, if you really must, grip the membrane between the nostrils with your finger and thumb and lead the animal by the nose, keeping its head well up (because if the head goes down, the animal is in a position of strength). Be very careful with the nose grip: brutally done it can induce not just tearful eyes but a nosebleed and it can also cause panic by impeding the breathing.

Bulls should only be handled by those with experience and confidence but who remember to treat them with considerable respect, however docile they might seem. Mature bulls are territorial and have a very strong sense of 'personal' fight-flight space (about 6m from the head if in a good mood) which you invade at your peril. Don't ever get in a situation where you can be cornered, but if you do, do *not* run: gradually back away to get out of his fight-flight space. In the field, if you do decide to run, a bull is less nimble going downhill.

Sheep

Confidence is the key to handling sheep; like cattle, they respond best to quiet, deliberate authority. Most breeds of sheep have a natural tendency to bunch together in the face of a predator (which might be what you are) and that is why sheepdogs are invaluable: their very presence keeps the sheep in a group. However, there are exceptions among the more primitive breeds: if you put a sheepdog to a flock of Soays, they will probably scatter in every direction, to the total bemusement of the dog, or might even outface it, which will ruin its confidence for life. A certain farmer in Argyllshire uses her *cat* if she wants to round up a lambing ewe in the dark: the cat investigates a ewe in difficulty, the farmer then shines a torch on the cat, which encourages the ewe to investigate the cat who, well trained, returns to the farmer, followed by the ewe, who can then be easily and quietly caught!

Sheep are much more likely than cattle to panic: they are well aware of their lack of defences. They are terrified of isolation and only begin to feel safe in groups of at least four or five: you will find one, two or three sheep very difficult to manage unless they are bottle-reared tamies (who will be so fearless as to be quite unmanageable anyway).

Most sheep have an overwhelming urge to follow sheep moving ahead of them. They react very quickly indeed to what they perceive as danger and their first reaction is to flee, preferably uphill or towards the light. They are extremely wary of entering a dark place, even their own shadows, and will go forward much more readily if they can see a possible opening ahead of them.

Crooks are useful aids for catching individual sheep, either by the neck or, with care, just above the hock. Make your initial approach from behind, to take advantage of the sheep's blind spot. If you put one hand under its jaw and hold the head a little higher than the back line, you should be able to control the sheep.

Once a sheep is down, it tends to resign itself to its fate. To 'cast' a light sheep, stand with your knees close to its left side and your left hand under its chin. Put the other arm over its body and take hold of a fold of wool and loose skin low on the right flank so that you can lift that hindleg off the ground and simultaneously nudge the body with your knees so that the sheep sags. Gently turn it to sit on its rump with its shoulders resting between your knees. With a heavier sheep, adopt the initial stance but carefully turn its head to look back along its body and at the same time put your right hand on its tailhead to brace it towards the animal's face. The sheep will sag into a sitting position. Once the sheep sits, it will begin to relax.

In New Zealand, incidentally, they are perfecting ways of hypnotising sheep for shearing. Quite seriously. It is worth considering . . .

Goats

Goats are much less predictable than cattle or sheep: they seem to be more individual, not to say capricious, especially with strangers, and they are of course very agile indeed. They are more likely to face an attacker than flee and they are also full of curiosity, which is something you should exploit. If you walk away, they'll probably follow you, but they are highly suspicious of narrow passageways.

Goats tend to be smallholder animals and are therefore familiar with people and used to being handled from kidhood. Because of their ability to jump and climb, they are often tethered or housed rather than given the freedom of a fenced field. However, they can sometimes be trained to respect their boundaries by the simple expedient of introducing them to the limits of their territory. Go right around the field with them trotting along behind you, as is their wont, and pause at frequent intervals to let them nibble and browse the boundary. It sometimes works, as long as there is nothing of overwhelming interest beyond . . .

Horses

Whole books have been written about understanding the equine mind. Like other species, horses respond to firm but kind and gentle handling, in spite of a traditional belief that they need to be dominated and mastered by sheer force. Their first instinct in the face of danger is to flee but they are perfectly capable of fighting back with hooves and teeth if they must.

Donkeys (and mules) are much less nervous than horses and are almost bovine in their liking for a leisurely life. They respond very well to kindness, consideration, and a generally slow, steady attitude. Don't try to hurry them: give them plenty of time to proceed in their own deliberate way.

Pigs

Pigs are probably the most intelligent of the farm animals and the most individual. They are home-lovers and dislike being moved elsewhere, especially out of a nice dark pen into the light. Pigs put unexpectedly into an open space can panic: they might try to hide in undergrowth or rush back to their den and, unlike sheep and cattle, they tend to scatter rather than keep together. They are more easily driven in groups of three but treat them as individuals when herding them. Make friends with them anyway, with plenty of soft conversation and back-scratching.

It would be wise to have ample help on hand to move even a single pig and to plan your strategy in advance, preparing the route carefully by setting up barricades before the pigs are let out. Pigs are quite easily fooled into believing that if they cannot see through something they cannot push through it either, even if it is only as flimsy as hardboard or cardboard, but tie the barriers together anyway. Use pigboards to direct them, or batons if they are trained for the show-ring to respond to light taps on the shoulder. Food is always appealing but a pig is more likely to follow an alluring bucket if it has been deprived of food for twelve hours or more. A shooing noise usually helps to propel a pig forward, or if it is being really awkward put an empty plastic bucket over its face and walk it backwards. For loading, a pig is more willing to go up a ramp than down but would prefer to remain on the level; make sure, too, that the ramp can be raised quickly without the side barriers having to be laboriously dismantled.

If you want to catch a pig, or especially a piglet, catch it the first time or you never will. Piglets can move surprisingly fast and pigs will *think* quicker than you do — you will see it in their eyes as they plan the next move. Once caught, piglets will squeal blue murder but it is easy enough to carry a small pig bodily. Two people are needed to carry a weaner: one takes the front legs and the other the back legs. In the end it is usually easier to catch up small pigs than to lure them.

Poultry

The most important aid in handling poultry is darkness: they are instantly quietened when the light goes out or if they can be hooded in some way.

Handling facilities

There are many occasions on which animals need to be channelled, confined or secured for inspection, treatment, removal, loading and other management procedures. However well you understand animal behaviour and exploit it, you can save endless time, temper and frustration if you have adequate handling facilities to help you, even for only one or two animals. The main components of such facilities, however unsophisticated, are races and handling pens.

Races

A race is, essentially, two parallel lines of fencing not much wider than the animal, acting as a single-file channel leading to perhaps a crush to contain an individual, a holding pen for confining a group, or a ramp for loading. At a race entrance it is wise to have a funnel or fan-shape to encourage entry so that the animals follow a natural line into the more restricted race without baulking at a narrow entrance. Such funnels gather them imperceptibly into a forcing area where they are confined to wait their turn into the race, and it is handy to have some kind of movable back barrier to urge them forward when necessary.

In theory, the animals will obey the follow-my-leader pattern so that as long as the first animal enters the system the rest should want to go the same way. (Train one as a Judas leader if you can.) The race is designed for a single file: it should not be wide enough for two to enter abreast or for one to turn around in. Avoid right-angled bends, but a good design can incorporate a gentle curve to encourage animals to keep moving forward after their disappearing predecessors. There must be adequate access so that you can inspect or treat the animals if you are not using a crush.

Systems for sheep are similar to those for cattle but adjusted in proportion to the animals: most people use easily managed metal sheep hurdles (or wooden ones if you are lucky enough to have them). Remember that sheep prefer to move uphill and towards a horizon or towards other sheep, that they 'flow' better round curves, and that they decidedly want to move away from buildings and other things which make them nervous.

For pigs, the sides of a race must be solid rather than railed and the race needs to be quite short or the pigs will never go near it.

Crushes

A crush is effectively a cage, usually at the end of a race or else a self-contained portable unit. Manufactured crushes usually have adjustable sides of tubular rails so that the unit can be adapted to the size of a single animal and restrict its sideways movement. There are gates at head and tail which prevent the animal from moving to and fro and often the front gate is designed as a yoke to hold the animal's head kindly but securely so that any necessary treatment can be given. There must be easy access to all parts of the animal's body, either through the side rails or by leaning over the top. The

floor *must* be non-slip for the sake of the animal and the head yoke must have a quick-release mechanism just in case the animal goes down. The tailgate can be a simple bar or chain but there should be provision made for the operator to stand behind the animal (e.g. for artificial insemination) without being shoved from behind by the next animal in the race.

Dispersal area

Have a holding area immediately beyond the crush where animals which have already passed through the system can collect. The sight of them ahead will encourage succeeding animals to move forward into the crush.

Loading

You can load a number of animals directly from a race through a small dispersal area: this gives you the chance of weighing, assessing, identifying and so on before they are loaded. Or you could devise an alley leading directly to the foot of the loading ramp.

The more gradual the ramp's incline, the more likely the stock will be to go up it. Ideally, have an access platform which brings the animals to the level of the trailer's floor so that they are on something solid all the way, rather than trying to persuade them up a lorry ramp from ground level. Ramps always cause dismay: they can be slippery, they sound hollow and they wobble — definitely deemed unsafe by any sensible animal and doubly so by one already suspicious about disturbances to its familiar routines.

Hurdles and gates

Light tubular metal gates and hurdles have endless uses in livestock handling. They can form temporary pens, indoors or outdoors, by being placed across a corner making a triangle or square or, in parallel to one wall, a stall with a tail chain at the rear. In rounding up sheep, metal or light cleft-wood hurdles are invaluable as portable aids to cut off escapes, block bolt holes, pen animals in a corner of the field, or channel them from one field to another across a track. Hurdles can also be carried as herders, rather like pig boards.

Movable posts

There was a useful tip in *Farmers Weekly* in 1979 (the magazine was running an invaluable 'fiver idea' series to which practical farmers contributed their very original and ingenious suggestions) sent in by a cattle farmer in Tamworth who often needed to divide his large yard to keep groups of animals separate. Strong metal pipes are set in concrete bases moulded in old lorry tyres so that they can easily be rolled into a new position. A chain is hung from the top of this portable post and supports scaffold pipes or forestry rails at various heights

Sheep dip

The aim of dipping is to control parasites by immersing the sheep in an approved chemical solution for a statutory period during which the sheep's head must be ducked at least once to soak the head and ears and the animal must be manipulated to ensure that the dip penetrates right through the entire fleece to the skin. It is no fun at all for the sheep or for the handlers, and every effort should be made to minimise stress to both parties by thinking carefully about the design of the whole dipping system, from collection to immersion and dispersal.

Ideally the sheep should be lowered gently into the dip and the exit ramp should be battened so that they can eventually clamber out with relative dignity. Sheep dislike swimming anyway and will not voluntarily enter water, which is little wonder when you imagine the extra weight of a saturated fleece, and they certainly do not like staying in for a whole minute, especially if at the same time they are being chivvied and dunked. It can be difficult, and stressful, to keep a sheep in a short bath when the animal's main aim is to regain dry land as soon as possible, but the longer the length of the bath, the longer it takes the sheep to swim it. Given space, the dip could be up to 30–40m long, or could curve around the handlers in a circle.

Permanent dips for larger flocks are set in concrete, with somewhere for handlers to stand along the length so that they can dunk and control the sheep. Naturally there needs to be a drainage system which prevents the solution from entering the watercourses, and you need to think about where the dipped sheep will drip off the excess liquid afterwards before they are returned to the field: it makes sense to channel the run-off back to the dipper. You should also think carefully about the storage of concentrated dip, which can be quite a dangerous substance.

Many farmers use portable dips and it is often worth a smallholder's while to make arrangements with them for the dipping of a handful of sheep. Specialist smallholding suppliers (see Addresses) offer a good range of small-capacity dipping tanks made of fibreglass or polyethylene.

Other sheep handling equipment

Sheep are popular livestock for smallholders and at least one long-established supplier offers guillotine-type exit gates and a complete sheep-handling kit for small flocks including hurdles and linking stakes, stop gates and two-way drafting gates (which are placed in a run to divert sheep to either side) — a system which has all sorts of uses on a sheep holding. They also offer sheep turning crates used to restrain sheep on their backs for foot care, veterinary treatment and general inspection: they are particularly useful when only one pair of hands is available. There are several designs on the market, ranging from the quite expensive rotating crates to the deckchair-like 'sheep sofa' which is a tenth of the price and weight of some crates and sits the sheep almost upright like a great aunt dozing off the effects of Christmas dinner, rather than turning it ignobly upside down with its legs in the air like a stranded beetle.

Tethering

Tethering is a cheap, versatile option for one or two animals where there are ample suitable grazing areas and if you have the time, inclination and self-discipline to shift the animal as often as necessary and to check frequently that all is well with it. Almost any kind of amenable animal can be tethered — guard dogs, goats, horses, donkeys, pigs, bulls, housecows, sheep — but success depends to some extent on the breed, temperament and training of the animal. Bear the following points in mind:

★ Avoid getting the tether rope or chain tangled around itself, around its post or a stump or bush, or around the animal.

★ Make sure that the animal, especially a goat, does not either strangle itself or slip off its collar or harness.

★ Give easy access to shade on hot days (remembering that the sun moves round!), shelter in rough weather, and ample fresh drinking water at all times — but if the water is in a portable containers put it at the extreme range of the animal's tethered reach so that it cannot be tipped over or fouled.

★ Beware of vehicle exhaust fumes if the animal is grazing verges — and beware, too, of accidents or vandals in such situations.

★ Watch out for predators, including playful dogs: your animal will be unable to escape.

★ Watch out for hazards such as ditches and slopes.

Tethering equipment has three components: a post, a line and a collar or harness. Posts, unless they are numerous and permanent, need to be easily re-sited but strong enough to stay in the ground under the strain of a tugging animal. The screw-in type used for guard dogs might be suitable for a goat but is not substantial enough for a cow. Try a flat-headed iron stake or crowbar which can be driven into the ground, though it will be rather cumbersome to shift, or scan the smallholder catalogues for something more convenient. A running tether, for example, would not need to be moved so frequently: the swivel link at the end of the tether line runs along a wire stretched between two posts.

Lines can be of rope but are better of chain, which will not get itself tied in knots. You must have a swivel system at both ends of the line so that it stays untangled. Solder a strong swivelled spring-clip to one end of the line to attach to the harness or collar; solder a large iron ring at the other end which can be slipped over the post and can swivel around it (as long as it can't swivel right up and off it). Even better is a chain with a built-in central swivel as well. The length of the line depends partly on how often you are prepared to shift the tethering and partly on what is manageable for the animal — say 6m, but use your own judgement. If the line is much more than 6m for a cow, she will spend all her time at its extremity trying to reach fresh grazing while trampling and dunging the rest of the circle to waste.

Goats are often tethered with a simple collar unless they are accident-prone (yes, they do hang themselves sometimes, or more often faint from the pressure of the collar on a nerve) in which case a headstall is better. Cows, too, can wear collars or heavy leather headstalls but bulls must have specially strong bull harnesses, sometimes with the line also running through the nose-ring, and pigs need body harnesses. Use you ingenuity with sheep, depending on whether or not they are horned and how skittish they are: train them to it by tethering for short periods initially. Collars on any animal should not fit too tightly but check that they cannot be slipped off.

Halters and rope tricks

You can buy readymade halters and headstalls or you can very quickly tie your own from a length of rope: the diagrams suggest some possibilities. A rope halter gives you more control than either a collar or a headstall because it automatically tightens when the animal fights it.

If you have tied an animal to an immovable object, however, especially if you are not present, make sure the length of rope is sufficient if it should fall or lie down. In any event, use a quick-release knot which will

ROPE TRICKS

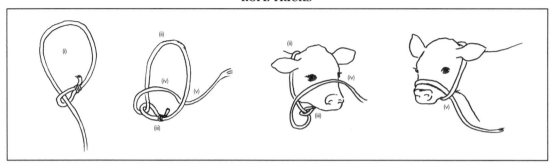

(a) Halter for calf or cow
   (i) Noose, formed by passing rope through firm loop
   (ii) Noose is slipped over animal's head, behind ears

(iii) Loop is under chin
(iv) Loose end taken over muzzle
(v) Loose end taken under halter's cheekpiece

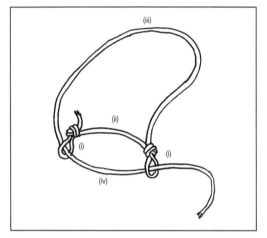

(b) Halter for horse
   (i) Two firm loops formed 10cm apart
   (ii) Section between loops taken over muzzle
  (iii) Loose end taken behind ears and down other
     side of face to pass through first loop
  (iv) Loose end taken under chin and through second
     loop

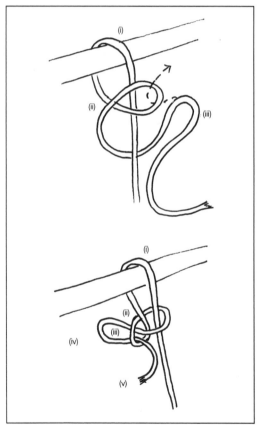

hold fast against the animal when it pulls away from the stanchion but which can be undone with a quick tug on the loose end if there is an emergency (see diagram). Don't tie the sort of knot that you cannot undo even with all the time in the world and have to resort to a knife.

By the way, if you've lost your knife and want to unbind a bale, use a spare piece of baler twine as a sawing blade. Baler twine is invaluable for so many roles: save it methodically by having a special twine nail in the

(c) Quick-release knot
   (i) Rope from animal passed round stanchion
   (ii) Simple twist formed, then loose end taken
     behind rope
  (iii) Loop formed and slipped into twist
  (iv) Loop (iii) remains protruding, while knot is
     tightened by pulling from direction of animal
   (v) Loose end can be pulled to release knot instantly

122

Rope halter on a Shetland sheep, tied to the rail with a quick-release knot.

barn. You can use it to tension an electric fence, to tie a gate 'temporarily', to make a knotted haynet, to plait as a rope or a doglead . . .

Basic livestock techniques

Bottle-feeding and bucket-rearing

There are dozens of old techniques for persuading a reluctant ewe or cow to accept a foster — enough for a whole book on the subject (yes, it is being written). Here are a couple of very simple ideas with sheep: try putting a little sugar on a newborn lamb's tongue and some on the ewe's udder if the lamb has been reluctant to suck, or, if you want to foster, tie a piece of string loosely around the back of the ewe's neck and into her mouth for a *short* period — she will be

so busy dealing with this irritation that she might ignore what is happening at the udder end. (Sorry!)

Drinking rather than sucking is an unnatural act to the very young and they need to be gently trained in the art. There are several problems: the physical act of sucking is quite different to that of lapping, for a start, and the attitude is all wrong in that a drinking animal has its head and neck inclined downwards rather than upwards, which can result in some of the milk being wrongly channelled into an undeveloped rumen rather than the abomasum. Drinking also encourages gulping and the intake of air or of too much milk at a time, and in addition the milk might be cold. All in all, the animal is more than likely to suffer digestive problems from bucket-rearing and in addition has the psychological trauma of being unable to satisfy its often desperate urge to suck.

To train a calf to drink from a bucket, quietly back the animal into a corner of its pen and squat down in front of it to block its escape. (Yes, additional trauma — motherless, and now trapped.) With the bucket of *warm* milk between your knees, offer the calf your fingers to suck — which it will probably accept eagerly. As it sucks, gently lower your hand into the bucket so that the calf is still sucking as its muzzle begins to dip into the milk — but take care that the liquid does not go up its nostrils. After a little, carefully withdraw your fingers. It will probably take two or three attempts before the calf will realise that the milk comes from the bucket and not from your fingers: you need to be very patient, calm and kind and be prepared to repeat the performance for several feeds until the calf drinks willingly. Make sure that it does not drink too fast or too much once it has learned how.

Bottle-feeding for an orphan piglet. *(Anna Oakford).*

There is usually less problem in persuading a very young animal removed from its mother to suck from an artificial teat, especially if there is a drop of milk on the teat to encourage it. Be very gentle and patient: the youngster is already under stress at being parted from the mother. Gently work the teat into its mouth but do not try to force it in and do not persist if it becomes a struggle. Try again later when it is hungrier. Think about the stance of a suckling animal: its head is generally craning upwards towards the udder and that is the attitude to be encouraged for bottle-feeding as well.

Equipment which satisfies the sucking urge can be any kind of bottle with a teat of appropriate size (and well sterilised every time) or a bucket with a teat fixed underneath. There are all sorts of multiple systems on the market — often known as lamb bars or 'calfeterias' to which several animals can help themselves when they wish, but it is more difficult to assess whether each individual is receiving its rightful share. If you are looking after small numbers, it is much better to feed individually: not only can you ensure that feeding is appropriate but you can also get to know the animal well enough to spot problems at an early stage.

Very weak lambs might need feeding by stomach tube and this requires skill and great care. A soft rubber tube of appropriate dimension is eased down the animal's gullet (but *not* its windpipe) and the milk (usually colostrum) is gently and slowly poured into a funnel at the top or with a syringe. Lubricate the tube first by gently drawing it across the lamb's tongue. If it coughs, or rolls its head, withdraw the tube and start again, being even more careful about how it is introduced. Keep hold of the free end to prevent the lamb from swallowing the whole thing.

Castration

There are three main methods of castration: the rubber ring, blunt pincers or the knife.

Rubber rings (also used to dock lambs) are applied with the aid of an elastrator: the ring is wrapped around the neck of the scrotum and in front of the rudimentary teats. Make sure that both testes have already descended into the scrotum before the ring is used. Castration by this method must be carried out during the first week of life (this is a legal obligation). Some people rubber-ring bull calves at a day old, which seems to be less distressing to them than a few days later, but it is decidedly more painful than surgical removal of the testes and this can be carried out when the calf is about seven weeks old (if it is really necessary), preferably with a local anaesthetic. Rubber-ring methods seem quick and simple for the stockman but in fact they do cause the animal pain immediately after the ring has been applied and also, in some cases, from ulceration two or three weeks later. Indeed, with lambs the immediate pain can be quite severe and the subsequent ulceration can induce tetanus.

An alternative is bloodless castration using blunt pincers to crush the spermatic cord and the testes' blood and nerve supplies. There is less risk of infection than with surgical castration but the period of distress and pain is longer. The burdizzo emasculator is a pair of very strong pincers with heavy, blunt jaws and a leverage system which greatly increases the force applied to the handles. One person holds the cord so that it does not slip away from the jaws while a helper works the handles. The testicles will gradually shrink and atrophy over a period of about a month but sometimes the instrument causes painful swelling and you need to be properly trained in its use.

The same applies to a knife: it requires skill to use one to remove testicles and also very high standards of hygiene, and the wound must be treated to prevent infection. It is an offence to castrate by any means after the age of two months (cattle) or three months (sheep) without the use of an anaesthetic, and at such an age only a veterinary surgeon can perform the operation.

Piglets used to be castrated at about a day old: the testicles were removed by being slowly pulled through scrotal skin incisions until the arteriovenous plexus broke. However, castration of any kind is less common in pig units today. Elastrators can be used within the first week of life but, like cattle, no method of castration can be used after a pig is two months old unless it is by a veterinary surgeon and using an anaesthetic.

De-horning

The removal of developed horns is unpleasant for the animal and for the operator — it usually results in a lot of blood. Don't attempt it yourself unless you are experienced, but talk to your vet if the job is really necessary.

Disbudding

Disbudding is the removal of an animal's horn buds before they can develop into horns and takes place almost as soon as the little knobs become apparent. Like any other assault, be it castration, docking or whatever else humans inflict on livestock during the course of management, disbudding causes distress as much by the act of capture and restraint as by the actual operation and its possible after-effects. When in doubt, don't.

Calves less than a week old can be disbudded with the use of caustic potash but this old method is rarely used now: it was painful and often failed to work anyway. The usual practice today is to use a hot iron and local anaesthetic when the calf is at least three weeks old and the buds are clearly evident, but you must have training in the techniques. The anaesthetic is injected close to each bud — and that is skilled work in itself. Of course, hygiene is vital when needles are being used. The hot iron (either electric or perhaps gas-operated) is applied firmly to each bud to kill it. There will be a period of irritation at least, probably for several days after the operation, and you should keep an eye out for infection or fly nuisance.

Kids are usually disbudded within a week of birth — their buds grow more vigorously than those of calves. The operation must be carried out by a vet, whatever a goat's age: a kid needs to be given a general anaesthetic before a hot iron is used to cauterise the bud.

Docking

The docking of piglets is to be discouraged. It used to be carried out routinely during the animals' first week of life because of behavioural problems with tail-biting, but it would be better to cure these with improved management techniques and environments instead.

It is more commonly practised with lambs, especially in lowland areas to reduce the risk of attracting blowflies to dungy backsides, and generally at the same time as castration using similar equipment — rubber-ringing with an elastrator to cut off the blood supply to the greater part of the tail, crushing with a bloodless castrator, cutting with a knife or using a sharp-edged hot iron. Check current legislation about the minimum length of the remaining tail stump. When rubber rings are used (which must be within the first seven days of life without anaesthetic and is usually during the first 48 hours), the tails usually drop off after a week or two, but the lambs will be very uncomfortable immediately after the rings are applied and they tend to rush about in some agitation. If a long, sharp knife is used instead, the bleeding will be negligible if the lambs are less than a month old.

Again, think about whether it is really necessary to carry out the operation. Certainly upland sheep are usually allowed to keep their tails long to protect themselves from the weather.

Dosing and drenching

Drenching is a method of getting liquids into the animal's stomach, for medicinal purposes or for a rapid nutritional boost (e.g. glucose for a sick animal). It involves slowly trickling the liquid down the gullet, taking great care not to choke it by pouring into the windpipe and lungs. Be especially careful if you are drenching a horse or pig.

For cattle, you can use any clean bottle but protect its open end with a piece of rubber piping if it is glass to prevent it being scrunched. Keeping all your movements reassuring and kind, stand beside the animal's head and reach one arm over its neck so that you can grasp and open its mouth by curling your fingers into the gap where there are no teeth. Tilt its head so that the neck is stretched but with the mouth no higher than its eye-level. Insert the neck of the bottle into the mouth from the other side, so that its tip is well to the back, having touched the roof of the mouth with it gently to warn the animal that something is coming so that it can close off its own windpipe and avoid choking. Keeping the neck and head extended in a line a few degrees above parallel to the ground, gradually trickle the liquid into the

back of the mouth, stroking the throat to encourage swallowing. Let the head drop immediately if the animal coughs or chokes.

An alternative to the nearest lemonade bottle is a drenching gun, typically used for dosing sheep or goats with anthelmintics and inserted into the mouth at the side, near the jaw hinge. But be careful in using a sheep drenching gun: it is possible to rupture the oesophagus, and you must be even more careful if using it for pigs.

Another 'gun' is the balling gun used for giving pills and boluses, by depositing them at the back of the throat. As with drenching, hold the animal's head slightly higher than the level of its back and rest the tip of the device on the back of the tongue. A bolus is a ball or cylinder of medicine in paste form for horses or cattle, and is often used as a slow-release medium for trace elements or anthelmintics.

Foot-care

Keeping feet healthy and adequately trimmed is essential to the wellbeing of the animal. Footbaths are easy enough to install at a point where the animals pass through regularly, or within a race, and even plain water in them will help to clean the claws and reduce the risk of disease. Sometimes the bath contains a very low percentage of formalin but it is easy to cause damage by too strong a solution or too frequent immersions.

Foot-trimming should be a regular routine rather than an emergency operation when something goes wrong: feet need to be checked long before an infection takes hold and need to be pared long before the animal becomes lame or stands unbalanced. Another part of good foot care is to make sure that the animal is not constantly standing in mud or wet conditions — the occasional walk on concrete is beneficial but, conversely, standing on nothing but concrete for long periods can be unforgiving. Check feet regularly for fungal problems: the cleavage between the two 'claws' is a perfect breeding ground, especially if muck can accumulate there.

Cattle and horses are usually handled blacksmith-fashion, with the animal's leg rested on your knee as you work and of

Foot-trimming for a sheep in the typical sit-back position for easy handling. *(Anna Oakford).*

course some king of restriction on movement (halter, head-yoke etc.). In the case of an uncooperative cow, use a rope to raise her leg to a convenient working height. Sheep can be put into a turnover crate or sheep sofa, or simply cast into the sitting position, but goats should not be cast: tether them and adopt the blacksmith style.

The aim in trimming is to reduce excessive hoof growth so that the animal's foot has a good weight-bearing surface, making sure that the wall of the hoof remains long enough to protect the softer sole. Be extremely careful not to cut into the quick. Use a very sharp horn-knife and a pair of hoof pincers.

Identification

However personally you know individual animals, there are often Ministry or breed society regulations which insist that each animal is permanently indentified by means of tattooing or tagging very soon after birth. In larger enterprises, it is also sensible to use semi-permanent methods of identification for management purposes; for example, using dyes or freeze-branding to stamp a very visible number on the flank, or ram raddle to identify tupped ewes, or tail-banding to identify cows at different stages of their lactation. Some farmers still use ear-notching (mainly pigs and sheep) or, for horned animals, horn etching.

Tattooing of the ear is carried out with the aid of a rather vicious looking tool which apparently causes only momentary discomfort. It is the most secure method of identification (tags can be torn off) but it can be quite difficult to read a tattoo in a dark-pigmented ear.

Ear-tags can be neat, stamped metal bands or all sorts of plastic devices inserted by punching holes or slits in the ear with special tools. Sometimes plastic tags are large enough to be read at a distance. The main problems with any kind of tag are that they can be ripped out of the ear, cause annoyance (especially the large ones) or if carelessly inserted can attract summer flies to a wound, but on the other hand some special ear-tags are designed to repel flies as they are impregnated with pyrethroids.

Notching is by means of a pair of special punch forceps and, again, it is said that the discomfort is no more than momentary. (Have you had your ears pierced?) It is certainly permanent but depends on a coding system if it is to be understood: numbers are represented by which ear and whereabouts on the ear the notch is placed and the system is rather like the binomial punched tape of old-fashioned computers — easy to read when you know how but meaningless if you do not.

Freeze-branding can remain legible for several years but does rather spoil the look of the beast! It is best on a dark animal: the freezing makes the existing hairs fall out, and the new hair which grows back in two to three weeks will be white ever after. For a white animal, the brand is left in place longer so that it destroys the actual hair roots and the result looks much like a hot branding. In America, they have been using hot laser branding, said to be so fast that the pain is over before the pain reflex is activated. Less drastic is the use of semi-permanent hair dyes — peroxide bleach lasts about a year, and black dye several months.

In New Zealand, they use cattle nose-prints for identification — as personal as human fingerprints, apparently.

Injections and vaccinations

Please ask your vet to teach you how to give injections and vaccinations safely and hygienic-ally, without causing bruises or abscesses, and make sure you understand the differences between subcutaneous or hypodermic (just under the skin), intramuscular (into a muscle), intravenous (into a vein) and so on. Also ask about the most appropriate site for an injection, whether for greatest efficiency, least pain or least damage to a potential hide.

Vaccination, which is immunisation against a specific infection, does not necessarily involve needles and can be as simple as pumping dust over the heads of poultry or as a nasal spray or oral dose. Where inoculation is necessary, it is usually subcutaneous: use your finger and thumb to raise a fold of skin at the appropriate site, forming a cavity under the skin. Insert the needle parallel to the body and into the cavity, without pen-etrating the underlying muscle. A sharp needle hurts least and is especially necessary with cattle, who can have very tough hides.

Milking

This is one of those arts best taught by experience but here are the main points of the technique. First wash the udder very clean — mainly for hygiene but also as part of a familiar ritual which encourages the animal to let down her milk. Without voluntary let-down, you will not be able to squeeze a single drop out of her.

Take a handful of teat, which should by now feel promisingly swollen with milk. The teat acts as a sort of storage vessel for milk let down from the udder and waiting to be drawn off by the animal's offspring, a mouthful at a time. Your aim is to trap the milk in this cistern with gentle pressure at the top of the teat and then persuade it down the teat channel and out the other end into your waiting bucket. The secret is to squeeze — quite gently but not gingerly — from the top downwards, starting with the pressure of your index finger and thumb (wrapped round the teat rather than pinching it between fingertip and thumbtip) and, maintaining the pressure at that point, gradually transferring it to second and then third finger (if the teat is long enough) so that the whole teatful is ejected in one satisfying spurt. Release the pressure so that the teat fills up again and repeat the process. Once the technique becomes second nature, the whole cycle will take less than a second. Use both hands, alternately and rhythmically, a teat in each. Udders and teats are quite easily damaged: do not pinch them or squeeze hard and do not tug the teat down like a bellrope.

Once let-down has been stimulated, let nothing distract you from emptying the udder. There should be a good, strong flow if your technique is right and the animal reasonably content but you will know that the job is almost complete when the flow subsides to a trickle and the 'bag' looks soft and loose rather than swelling. Massage the udder gently while you use finger and thumb to ease out or 'strip' what remains in the teat but do not be greedy for every last drop.

Shearing

During winter, the wool next to a sheep's skin becomes greasy and yellow ('yolk' is a common term for it). By late spring or early summer the yolk has 'risen': the greasy wool has been pushed up by new, white wool and it can now be shorn without the problems of yolk-clogged shears. In the old days it was customary to wash sheep a while before the rise, especially the fine wools like that of the Southdown which were rich with yolk; the yolk was given perhaps twelve days after

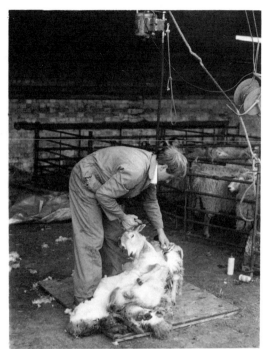

Shearing Portland sheep (a rare breed, helpfully horned) at Wimpole Home Farm. *(Anna Oakford).*

that in which to rise in the staple to give it softness and plasticity, then the fleece was shorn.

Do not attempt your own shearing until you have watched professionals at work and preferably attended proper classes. Sit the sheep up, leaning slightly backwards against your legs, and start with the belly wool, then the hind legs (up to and over the tail), then one side, the back, the neck and shoulders and the second side.

Teeth

Some people clip piglets' incisor teeth to prevent injury to the sow during suckling but it is yet another unnecessary infliction on the little ones. If it is practised, it should be done by a vet or skilled operator.

Cattle and sheep have no incisors on the upper jaw and no canines at all. It is usually only in sheep that teeth cause problems: older ewes become 'broken mouthed', that is they lose some of their lower incisor teeth prematurely and have difficulty in feeding. It is possible that some form of protein or mineral deficiency lies at the root of the problem. Breeding cows are usually culled as barreners long before their teeth let them down.

V Machinery

We live now in the age of the depletion of non-renewable energy sources, depending heavily on the internal combustion engine in particular as the driving force in agriculture. It is a very recent evolution: for centuries, farmers relied on muscle power — their own or that of oxen and, later, horses — to work the land and make use of its produce. When the oil inevitably dries up, perhaps the old and satisfying on-farm energy cycle will come into its own again — a few alternatives are considered in the final section of this book. For now, however, what are the possibilities for using petrochemically and electrically driven machines on the holding?

First of all, it depends on the type of enterprise. If the land is cultivated in some way you need more equipment and power than if you simply run a few animals on grass. In the latter case, you only need enough machinery to help you maintain the boundaries and perhaps to make your own hay rather than buying it in — and even today it is still practicable to do much of such work by hand or with the help of animal power.

The main requirement on many holdings is a machine which combines the ability to transport and to drive mechanical implements, though on some extensively managed livestock farms the first priority is a means of getting yourself to less accessible parts of the land as quickly and easily as possible, perhaps carrying animal feedstuffs or a few animals as well.

All-terrain vehicles

On the huge ranchlands of Australasia and America, horses are being replaced by rugged cross-country motorbikes that can carry a person (and a dog) at high speed across difficult terrain. The bikes are also used as cow-ponies to round up stock. This type of machine led directly to the more versatile, if not quite so nippy, all-terrain vehicle or ATV now seen on perhaps 20,000

All-terrain vehicle with small trailer, one of many attachments which can be used with ATVs. *(David Rayner)*.

agricultural and horticultural holdings in the UK.

Initially ATVs were developed for the American leisure market in a country where there is endless space and the challenge of terrain ranging from deserts and beaches to mountains. In the UK, too, they were at first bought for fun: bike riders thoroughly enjoyed whizzing across the fields and up into the hills, ostensibly to check on livestock, but very soon the two-wheeled motorbike became a three-wheeler — much more stable, able to stand upright without being supported and with an increasingly powerful engine so that it began to be a workhorse as well as a pony. Most of the machines were (and still are) produced by Japanese motor-cycle manufacturers, quick to respond to marketing opportunities, but it was British farmers who found imaginative uses for their ATVs and began to invent equipment for them.

Now most ATVs are four-wheeled, with either two-wheel or four-wheel drive, and the more powerful really have become trusty workhorses, though of course their capacity is limited in comparison with a tractor. At the time of writing, available machines range from nine to about 25 horsepower (17hp = 12kW, 21hp = 15kW), some of them offering up to ten gears, and are priced from about £2,000 to a little over £3,000 for four-wheelers. The very latest are six-wheeled, with drive through all the wheels. In the meantime the list of implements designed for ATVs grows substantially year by year.

As toys, ATVs are expensive, but as versatile workhorses they are a lot less expensive to buy new than a tractor and can perform many of the tasks needed on a smallholding: they get you about the place quickly, they can pull small trailers, they can be used for mowing, spreading slug pellets or fertiliser, trailing sprayers, pushing power brushes — there is a growing list of their applications, and indeed one of the main problems is that the vehicle seems so willing that people tend to exploit it to a much greater extent than they should. Also, each implement can cost up to half as much as the biggest ATV.

An important point in their favour, often at the top of the list for those who use them, is that they are still fun and exhilarating to ride. Of course there are drawbacks: they don't keep you dry in the rain, or warm in cold weather. Crash helmets are not essential but would be a wise precaution if you are working near low-branched trees and similar hazards, and would anyway keep your head dry and warm. Some of the machines have gauntlets which can be fitted to the handle-bars, too, and now cabs are being developed especially for ATVs, which might reduce a problem directly related to their 'fun' image, which does encourage slightly reckless driving, even when they are supposed to be working. The young of all ages love them: it is very easy to learn how to drive ATVs and they are much safer than two-wheelers, especially the four-wheelers which have virtually super-seded the lighter and less stable three-wheelers.

A more important problem is that just because they seem to be willing to work does not mean that they are able to control too heavy a load or to maintain the constant speed needed in the field for applying fertilisers and sprays. They can also be very noisy for constant work and you might need earmuffs.

Most of the vehicles now have integral carriers on the front and rear so that you can transport bits and pieces like fencing stakes, a couple of bales or bags of cake or the dog, and many now hitch up to the specially designed small trailers to increase their carrying capacity. The basic trailer is big enough for several bales (if the machine is powerful enough to take the drawbar pull) and can be fitted with sides to transport small livestock — very popular with outdoor pig farmers or for carrying sheep or a couple of calves. Some of the trailers have loading ramps and manually operated tipping bodies; some are four-wheeled rather than two-wheeled; some are designed so that the wheels do not protrude and catch you unawares through a narrow gap.

Pig and sheep farmers also appreciate the automated feedwagons; these are electronic-ally controlled dispensers which deposit measured amounts of food at measured intervals across the field, controlled without leaving the vehicle — a boon when you are giving supplementary feed to a playful herd of outdoor pigs, a greedy flock of ewes, a wary group of deer or suckler cows, or gamebirds perhaps. Several standard bales can be carried in trailers and even big bales can be transported by an ATV, one bale at a time on a towed two-wheel chassis with a spike.

You can buy a tandem axle chassis for ATVs, fitted with its own engine to drive a sprayer or spreader but really only suited to flat land, even with the most powerful machine. However, they are very useful indeed for wet-weather applications, particularly of slug pellets, as they can be run on the land when a tractor would cause wheel damage. Wet-weather work is perhaps one of their most useful roles, especially for contractors: ATVs can be on the land when tractors should be firmly shut up in their sheds.

You can buy independently powered rotary or flail mowers (note that at present the ATV is not expected to power the implements) which are ideal for parks and golfcourses or for topping small paddocks but tend to give up on long wet grass. They can be rear-mounted — and you can also find rear-drawn ballast rollers and chain harrows for ATV use — or front-mounted, as are power brushes, yard scrapers, snow blades, weed wipers and so on.

ATVs are essentially off-road vehicles, and in the UK you may only take them on the public highway for the purposes of agricultural, horticultural or forestry work. They can be made roadworthy by fitting a special road-kit (rearview mirrors and legal lights in addition to the built-in headlights and the lamp which can be handheld for rabbit shooting at night) but can only be driven at legal tractor speeds on the road, preferably with some kind of warning, as they are so much smaller than tractors. They are also less easy to steer on hard surfaces, even when you fit more roadworthy tyres. They can be taxed and insured either as agricultural or as 'private light goods' vehicles

like the family car. Crash helmets are not at present compulsory for ATV drivers on the public highway but would be a sensible precaution — there is not much to protect you in an accident. An alternative to fitting a road-kit is to transport the ATV in a Land Rover's trailer.

If you are interested in ATVs, it is important to consult a reliable dealer with a good range of makes and models and to heed the advice given on the most suitable machine and implements for your situation. In particular, respect the limitations of the machine and do not demand too much of it. It will do the work, like any willing horse, but . . .

Tractors

Tractors range in size and capacity from small garden ride-on mowers to enormous multiple-wheeled giants of breathtaking traction power. Smallholders might seize upon the idea of compact tractors as ideal for their needs, but quite honestly you would do better to buy a good secondhand Fergie. Compact tractors are used on some horticultural enterprises, or for pottering around livestock buildings, but they are expensive. Your dealer can advise you.

'Real' tractors have been familiar in this country since the Second World War, though they began to make their impact after the First. The giants at the top of the range today are terrifyingly expensive, but there are plenty of more modest models suitable for general farmwork and smallholdings. The problem for smallholders is one of being over-powered: it is increasingly difficult to find conveniently small tractors of the type that used to be so common. There is still much affection for the old models, like the faithful grey 'Fergie', and there is a thriving secondhand market — but buyer beware! Unless you know your engines, you might be spending more on repairs and hard-to-find replacements than you have saved.

Today's tractors use diesel fuel, though many of the older models are petrol-driven.

Diesel engines are more efficient, more economical, quick to reach full power from a cold start, relatively troublefree — and initially more expensive to buy but usually worth it. However, many smallholders will probably have a friendly old petrol-driven machine which has to be coaxed into action, perhaps with the aid of a trusty crank and certainly with the need for a knack.

Make sure that all fuel is cleanly stored and cleanly transferred to the tractor's fuel tank (use a filter). Make a habit of clearing the storage tank of sludge or water before a new delivery is made, and anyway let the new fuel settle for 24 hours before you draw any off.

Starting up

To start a diesel-engine tractor: check that the gear is in neutral, and/or push down the clutch pedal; open the throttle about halfway; set the STOP control to the RUN position and turn the ignition switch and the starter switch (the latter is usually a further movement of the ignition key, like many cars). Some models have cold-start aids. If the engine won't start within half a minute, let it rest a few seconds before trying again. If you get really fed up, try an aerosol burst of quick-burning ether into the air cleaner or manifold inlet.

To *stop* the tractor, pull out the STOP control knob to cut off the fuel supply; wait until the engine stops before putting the gear lever into neutral. To *park*, follow the stopping procedure and then apply the handbrake; leave the gear lever in neutral (or PARK) and make sure the implements have been safely lowered to the ground.

The *throttle* sets the engine speed. Where there is a choice, use the hand throttle for continuous work like ploughing or the foot throttle (which can override the hand throttle) for intermittent work like loading manure or driving along the road.

The *clutch* pedal on the left is used to engage drive between the engine and gearbox. Some tractors have a dual clutch: it is pushed halfway down to stop the wheels but all the way down to disconnect drive to the

PTO (power take off) shaft. Others have an independent PTO clutch.

The PTO is engaged or disengaged with a lever independently of the transmission clutch. The PTO shaft is used to drive all sorts of equipment and is also useful for emergency generators during power cuts. In the days before electricity became more popular in the farmyard, belt pulleys fitted to the PTO shaft (or direct to the gearbox) were used to drive stationary equipment such as sawbenches. The PTO usually has two speeds: 540 or 1,000 rpm.

There are usually two *gear levers*: one selects the range (high or low) and the other the gear ratio. The main selections are forward, neutral and reverse and most tractors give a choice of perhaps eight forward gears and four reverse. Gears should only be selected when the tractor is stationary unless it is a change-on-the-move model. Choose a low gear before going down a slope.

There are usually two types of *brake*: a handbrake for parking and a pair of brake pedals (one for each rear wheel). By using the pedals separately, the tractor can be more easily manoeuvred in restricted spaces. For driving on public roads, however, the two pedals must be locked together. If there is no handbrake, the pedals will have a latching system for parking.

The *differential* allows the drive wheels to turn at different speeds when cornering. The *differential lock* or 'DIFF-LOCK' prevents this in order to reduce possible wheelspin in difficult conditions and thereby increase traction. The DIFF-LOCK is usually engaged by means of a foot pedal, unless it is semi-automatic. It must be disengaged when turning a corner: if it does not do so automatically, release it by pressing one brake pedal and pushing down the clutch.

Apart from driving stationary equipment, the main roles of a workhorse tractor are to pull, to drive trailed implements and to lift. For these activities it also needs a *drawbar* for pulling (a swinging drawbar is used for heavier equipment), a *three-point linkage* for implement attachment and an *automatic pick-up hitch* so that trailed implements can be attached while the driver remains seated, lowering a hook and guiding it under and into a ring on the implement's drawbar then lifting it and locking it into the raised position.

Above all, it needs a *hydraulic system* for lifting and lowering mounted implements — operating forklifts, loaders, tipping trailers, controlling the cutting height of forage harvesters and hedge trimmers and driving certain implements, for example, including the three-point linkage and the automatic pick-up hitch. The basic controls for the hydraulic system are the *draft control* (which ensures a regular depth for soil-working implements), the *position control* (to hold implements at a constant position above ground) and the *remote control* for work such as tipping trailers.

Never put yourself between tractor and implement but work from the side for safety. To hitch up a mounted implement: reverse up to the implement, aligning squarely to it rather than attempting to heave the implement into position by brute strength. Attach the linkage in the correct order — always left first, then right, then top. With a swinging drawbar, remove one half of the tractor drawbar's jaw; if you used double jaws on both drawbars you would probably shear the pin.

Tyres should be fitted so that, viewed from the rear, the arrow pattern of the tread points upwards. In the field, use the lowest recommended tyre pressures to give the greatest grip and the most efficient traction, and improve the latter on rough land by weighting the wheels either by filling the tubes three-quarters full with water (add calcium chloride to the water in frosty weather) or by bolting cast-iron disc weights on the rear wheels. The front wheels can be weighted to counterbalance heavy implements mounted at the rear. In wet conditions, spiked strakes can be fitted to rear wheels for better traction to supplement the diff-lock, and extra rear wheels are sometimes added for very soft or marshy ground. Cage wheels will reduce soil compaction: they are treadbars of tubular angle-iron set on large metal wheelrim frames.

Tractor safety and law

Tractors are not toys and have been the direct or indirect cause of many unpleasant, crippling or fatal accidents on the farm, which is particularly traumatic if children are involved. Always be alert for children in the area, especially if you are reversing. Children younger than 13 are not allowed to drive or ride on tractors or farm machinery by law but can ride in or on an empty or part-filled trailer if it has four sides projecting above the floor or load. Nobody — child or adult — should ever ride on the drawbar or linkage when something is being towed. There is also a legal responsibility to make full use of equipment guards where appropriate and all tractors must now be fitted with a protective overhead roll-bar or a cab.

On the public highway, the maximum legal speed for a tractor is 20 mph, or 12 mph if it is towing two trailers. On a dual carriageway, travelling at less than 25 mph, the vehicle should display a flashing amber beacon as a warning. All lights should be in proper working order, mirrors fitted appropriately, windscreens clear, steering and tyres in good condition, trailers properly braked, brake pedals latched together and, of course, loads secure. The law requires you to remove mud and other farm debris deposited on the highway before it becomes a hazard to other road users.

You need a registration plate, an insurance certificate, a road fund licence (or exemption certificate) and a driving licence. In 1930, highway regulations caused some irritation and an article in *The Field* at the time grumbled thus:

'Now it seems that the farmer's tractor must be insured against third party risks, even if it only runs occasionally on a public road to get from one field to another. This is likely to cost him about 15s a year. And in addition the tractor driver must have a motor-driving licence. This seems rather a farce. Few tractor drivers can drive a car. But the inevitable must be accepted, and farmers have to fall into line and pay out another 20s a year for the privilege of running a tractor across the public road. Of course, to defeat the law, the tractor could be run up on to a trolly and pulled across by horses.'

Two weeks later *The Field* was complaining that police in some areas were warning farmers that the new Road Traffic Act required that 'a spare man should be carried in any trailer, however small, which they use behind their cars on market days' to take calves, hens and other produce to market. Such people, the magazine declared, would have 'no man to spare for joy-riding' but, happily, the Ministry of Transport was persuaded that two-wheeled trailers behind private cars could be exempt from the regulation.

Implements

Ploughs

Ploughs can be trailed, or mounted or semi-mounted on a tractor's hydraulic linkage at the front, with their own wheel supports, or are push-pull types with one on the rear linkage and a second on the front. Trailed ploughs are generally drawn by crawlers (tracked vehicles).

Conventional ploughs have only right-hand mouldboards (the mouldboard cuts the furrow slice and turns it) but the heavier and more expensive *reversible ploughs* have right-hand and left-hand mouldboards to work up and down the same furrow, leaving a more level field for subsequent cultivations. Some ploughs have large rotating *discs* rather than mouldboards but these do not 'bury the trash'. *Chisel ploughs* are heavy-duty cultivators with tines bolted on a very strong tractor-mounted frame, with the working depth hydraulically controlled (though larger ones have wheels), and they are sometimes used instead of mouldboard ploughs if there is not much trash to bury or tackle the heavy work of breaking up stubbles. If all but three of the tines are removed, chisel ploughs can be used as *subsoilers* which, with very strong tines set a metre apart, are drawn through the ground to half a metre deep to break up the subsoil pans which can form if the land is ploughed to the same depth year after year. A *mole plough* is used for draining heavy land: it consists of a torpedo-shaped share which, set on a very strong leg, forms tunnels running at an angle to the land-drain system; it can be trailed or mounted on the three-point linkage and needs a powerful tractor or a crawler.

To prepare for ploughing, attach the implement to the three-point linkage in the right order: first the lower lefthand link, then the lower righthand and finally the top link. Use the draft control to set the ploughing depth; adjust the pitch, the front furrow width and the headstock level; set the coulter; check the wheeltrack setting; see that the mouldboards are parallel to each other.

Cultivators

The main role of cultivators of any kind is to break up clods and stir the soil. The implements, of various widths, consist of a framework of tines which might be set rigid, or strongly sprung where there is interference from tree roots and stones, or sprung and constantly moving to pulverise the clods at high speed — ideal for pulling weed rhizomes to the surface. The depth of work is controlled by means of the tractor linkage or by wheels on the implement.

Rotary cultivators or *rotavators* are PTO-driven, with the working depth controlled by skids or landwheels: they are useful for creating a good tilth in difficult conditions, its fineness being controlled by the tractor's forward speed (the faster, the coarser). They are good for burying crop remains and can also control weed rhizomes if the field is passed over several times at intervals of 10–14 days so that the rhizomes are chopped up and exposed to dry as they sprout, or are buried. A rotary cultivator can replace a whole set of seedbed implements. The flat blades are L-shaped and are rotated at speeds of 90–240 rpm, throwing the soil against a flap at the rear to help break the clods. They need a tractor of about 150hp.

Harrows

Harrows are used to prepare a fine tilth and to consolidate it by shaking down the soil. The most common type has zigzags of staggered tines. The tines themselves are straight and can vary in length and strength. *Dutch harrows*, used for bashing clods and levelling seedbeds, are heavy wooden frames set with spikes. *Chain harrows* are rectangles of short, flexible links, spiked on the underside, which can ride over uneven or grassed surfaces. *Knife tines* are used in improving matted grassland. Power-driven *reciprocating harrows* and *rotary harrows* are used to prepare fine seedbeds on heavy soils. *Disc harrows* are gangs of saucer-shaped discs, each 30–60 cm in diameter, which cut and consolidate the soil; the more angled the set, the greater the depth of the work and the more effectively they can break clods, especially when the rear discs are more angled than the front ones. Disc harrows are used for preparing seedbeds after grassland has been ploughed.

Rollers

Rolling consolidates the top few centimetres of the soil, keeping it in contact with plant roots (for example, after frost has lifted them) and helping the soil to retain more moisture. Rollers are also used to crush clods or break surface crusts ('caps') but should not be used when the soil is wet. Flat-surfaced rollers have largely given way to ribbed Cambridge or *ring rollers* which consist of several heavy iron wheels or rings, each about 7 cm wide with 4 cm ridges and moving independently of each other. Ribbed rollers leave a nicely corrugated seedbed for grass and clover. A *furrow press* is a very heavy ring roller for compressing the furrow slices after ploughing.

Drills and seeders

Typical drills consist of a hopper with a mechanism which feeds the seed into tubes leading to coulters (blades) which mark a shallow furrow into which the seed is delivered and then covered with the help of tines on the coulters or a separate set of harrows. The differences between various drills lie in the type of feed mechanism and the type of coulters. *Combine drills* can feed fertiliser and seed simultaneously, while *direct drills* are able to place seed into undisturbed soil

with the help of very heavy coulters which cut seeding slots as they work.

Seeder units are individually wheeled for each seed row and are used to space seeds in the row in the case of vegetable and root crops in particular. Each unit has its own hopper, feed mechanism, coulter and seed-covering device. Anything from perhaps five to twelve units are attached to a toolbar mounted on the tractor.

The two main arts in using drills and seeders are to ensure a constant rate of accurately assessed seed delivery and to join each pass accurately without overlapping or leaving unwanted gaps between the bouts. Sowing rate is calibrated before the work starts and is checked as accurate by either test-drilling a measured area of the field with a measured quantity of seed or, in the yard, by jacking up the drill and turning its wheel a calculated number of times (equivalent to the number of turns which would cover a certain area in the field) and catching and weighing the amount of seed it delivers.

In many cases the tracks of the drill wheels in the field will act as a guide for the adjacent pass, or you can use drill markers, which are adjustable discs or pointed tines on each side of the drill.

Grass seed is often broadcast rather than drilled; that is to say, it is not sown in deliberate rows.

Broadcasters

Broadcasters are mainly used for distributing fertilisers. They consist of a hopper, usually tractor-mounted (though the biggest ones might be trailed) with one or two spinning discs or an oscillating spout to distribute the material, driven from the PTO or perhaps with hydraulic motor drive. ATV-mounted broadcasters have their own motors. Two factors control the application rate: the forward speed of the vehicle (faster for a lower rate) and the adjustment of the amount of material passing from the hopper to the distributors (the larger the opening, the higher the rate). Different models give different spreads for different materials and you need to mark the field so that you neither overlap nor leave gaps between each bout — try putting marking stakes at regular intervals on the headland, for example, and avoid working in windy conditions.

Sprayers

Crop sprayers of many kinds are used to apply chemical solutions for the control of weeds, insect pests and fungal diseases, or liquid fertilisers. They basically consist of a tank, a PTO-driven pump with a relief valve to control the working pressure, and filters to keep bits of dirt away from the fine spraybar nozzles. Application rates are controlled by nozzle size, spraying pressure and the tractor's forward speed. As with fertiliser application, it is important to be able to maintain a constant speed so that application rates are consistent. It is also necessary to ensure that the height of the spraybar is such that the spreads from each nozzle just meet above the crop or target weeds. Most sprayers are tractor-mounted and the smallest, with a tank capacity of 200 litres, are ideal for 16–20 hp tractors, whereas trailed or self-propelled sprayers are more suited to large arable holdings. It is of course most important to check wind direction and strength while spraying to avoid drift: a weedkiller designed for a cereal crop could wipe out your neighbour's vegetables, and an insecticide could devastate local bees or your children's goldfish. Those who handle agricultural pesticides of any kind, whether applied by machine or by handheld equipment, are by statute required to have proper instruction in their use and clearly will make a point of reading the manufacturers' instructions with great care, not only for advice on application rates and timing but also on the storage and disposal of the chemicals. Some are so dangerous that you need a stand-by respirator if you are driving in an enclosed safety cab.

Loaders

If you have more manure than you can handle with a fork and barrow, you will fir d good use for a tractor-mounted front-end loader operated by the tractor's hydraulic system. The loader can be fitted with implements such as manure forks, silage grabs, grain or root buckets and bale loaders.

However, take care in using a front-end loader: it obviously shifts the centre of gravity of the tractor, especially when the arms are fully raised and fully laden, and you need to use six-ply front tyres at higher pressures than for fieldwork, and to counter-balance the front weighting at the rear. Some farmers use self-propelled rough-terrain forklifts or skid-steer loaders for handling larger quantities of manure. Another aid to handling manure and slurry is the rear-mounted or front-mounted yard scraper, and there is a version suitable for use with ATVs as well. Tractors can also take rear-mounted loaders or mounted grabs.

Buckrakes, which are forks consisting of several strong horizontal tines bolted to a bar pivoting on a frame attached to the three-point linkage, have endless uses on farms large and small: they can pick up all manner of materials from the ground, lift them up and carry them for depositing elsewhere by tilting the tines by means of a lever. They can be rear-mounted or front-mounted: the former gives greater tractor stability and the latter makes it easier for the driver to see what is happening.

Muck-spreaders

PTO-driven manure spreaders are trailed implements which either shred the material, delivering it from the rear of the spreader by means of floor conveyors and rotors, or they use high-speed chain flails to throw the stuff out sideways from a cylinder-shaped trailer open to one side only.

Slurry spreaders are basically trailed tanks, pump-loaded and discharged in the field by pressure pumps or by gravity.

Hay-making

There are basically three types of grass mower, but the old cutter-bar types have largely been replaced now by rotary and flail mowers. *Rotary mowers* are PTO-driven and can be mounted on the three-point linkage or trailed; some are front-mounted. They include *drum mowers*, with up to three large-diameter rotors, each with from three to six cutting blades (like those of a rotary garden mower), or *disc mowers*, with a series of smaller diameter discs set on a cutter bar, each with two or three blades. *Flail mowers* have swinging flails on a high-speed rotor: they bruise the grass as it is cut and leave the swath nicely fluffed up. *Cutter-bar mowers* have a reciprocating knife mechanism driven by the PTO and must be kept sharp with a knife grinder or flint; they are slower to work with than rotary mowers and make heavy work of heavy crops.

Tedders are used to lift and open the swath to let the air circulate through it; they are PTO-driven and can be mounted or trailed. There are many designs but they are basically spring-tined rotors on either a vertical or a horizontal axis. *Finger-wheel turners* are hydraulically mounted on a frame so that they can 'float' on unlevel surfaces as their spring tines turn the swath and move it sideways.

Silage-making

Silage crops are usually cut with *mower conditioners*, which both cut the crop and bruise it to release sap and speed the drying process. Conditioners might be PTO-driven (mounted or trailed) or can be separate machines. After wilting, the crop is picked up with a *forage harvester*, which can be mounted, trailed or self-propelled, and which chops the crop as it is lifted and then blows it into a high-sided trailer towed by a separate tractor running in tandem. The main types of mechanism in forage harvesters are the flywheel chop and cylinder chop. The older type is the flail forage harvester, which does not chop the crop but simply lacerates it and is only suitable for silage made in pits and clamps, which means that it is probably just what you need.

Alternatively, for smaller areas, the crop can be cut with the type of mower used for haymaking and, after wilting, collected from the swath with the aid of a buckrake, or you can use a *forage wagon*. This is a high-sided wagon with a pick-up cylinder at the front to lift the crop to a chopping mechanism and thence into the wagon, which has a moving floor conveyor for emptying the load through its rear door into the silage store.

Balers

Balers are sheer magic: they take in loose hay or straw and, presumably with the aid of a team of gnomes hidden within, they bundle it tightly into carefully shaped bales bound with wire or twine in moments and neatly deposited on the ground or on a sledge. *Pick-up balers* produce traditional sized bales — anything from 0.3 to 1.3m long and typically twice as long as wide (the most common size is 92cm long, 46cm wide and 36cm deep). *Big balers* produce the monsters of more recent years, either cylindrical (0.9–1.8m in diameter and 1.2–1.5m wide) or rectangular (0.8–1.6m wide, 0.6–1.3m deep and 1–2.5m long). The weight of a standard bale might be somewhere around 25kg, and that of a big bale at least twice as much for straw or up to four or five times the weight for hay.

Several adjustments can be made to a pick-up baler: the pick-up height is set by means of a lever or wheel at the side of the pick-up cylinder so that the collecting tines are about 10cm above ground; the packers, which pass the collected crop into the bale chamber, are adjusted for different types of crop and need to be re-set if the bales emerge curved (which means that the packer fingers are throwing too much material to one side of the chamber); the density or compactness of the bale, and hence its weight, is controlled by adjusting screws at the end of the chamber to increase or decrease resistance against the bales (or you can bolt wedges on either side of the chamber to make a more compact bale) — hay bales, being much heavier than straw bales anyway, need less resistance, and even more so if heating is to be avoided when the crop is still a little damp. The bale length is adjusted by a stop on the metering wheel linkage.

There are many moving parts in a baler and therefore there is the potential for something to go wrong. Make sure that the equipment is greased daily, or even twice a day; check gearbox oil levels and tyre pressures weekly; see that drive chains and belts are correctly tensioned and keep the plunger knife sharp. The plunger is a ram which compresses the bale; the knife, on the pick-up side of the plunger, cuts the crop wads against a fixed knife.

To make sure of well-shaped bales, check that the feed rate into the chamber is even: curved bales might be the result of setting the density screws differently or failing to adjust the packer drive linkage for lighter or heavier crops. A nasty clattering noise means that the pick-up cylinder's clutch has slipped because the tines have caught the ground or the pick-up is overloaded — and a sudden overload can lead to the breaking of the single shear bolt which transmits the tractor's power to the baler's flywheel. Broken needles can occur because of mistiming with the movements of the plunger (check that the setting is correct) and bad tying can sometimes arise from the poor quality of the twine or incorrect threading of the knotters. Uneven feed to the chamber might result in bales of different lengths, while ragged bale edges mean that the plunger knife is probably blunt or wrongly set: the clearance between the knives should be about one millimetre.

A *bale sledge* can be towed behind the baler to collect bales as they emerge and deposit them in regular formations for easier loading rather than the bales being scattered at random all over the field. They can be used with special pick-up attachments on a tractor loader which can lift the complete formation.

Harvesters
Combine harvesters for cereals, seed crops, oilseeds, peas and beans are beyond the scope of this book, and so are the many types of specialist root harvesters and planters.

Hedge-cutting and ditching
The neatest tractor-cut hedge is produced by the use of hedgers with reciprocating knife cutter bars. They cannot deal with thicker stems and many farmers therefore prefer to use flail rotor cutters — which can indeed smash their way through the larger stems but leave them not only looking terrible but also so badly damaged that the hedge is likely to succumb to disease.

Both types of cutter are set on hydraulic arms and can be angled to cut the different faces of a hedge or the sides of a ditch and bank. A flail, for example, usually has two cutting speeds, the higher for hedge-cutting and the lower for dealing with grass.

Ditches can be cleaned out or freshly dug with the aid of tractor-mounted diggers connected to the three-point linkage or, for substantial work, industrial tractor diggers with front-loader buckets and perhaps a trench digger at the rear.

Small excavator for renovating a pond or cleaning out ditches.

Trailers

There are tractor-drawn trailers for every conceivable need, either attached automatically with a pick-up hitch ring or linked to a swinging drawbar by a jaw-type hitch. Swinging drawbars allow the necessary height adjustment and sideways movement needed for trailing heavier equipment, and the type of drawbar attached to the lower hydraulic links on small tractors should only be used for trailing light implements. The automatic pick-up hitch is operated by the hydraulics system: you can remain in your seat while you manoeuvre the hook under the ring on the implement's drawbar, then lift the hook hydraulically and lock it in the raised position. Jaw-type hitches need a screw jack to lift or lower the drawbar.

Note that the drawbar horsepower is always less then the brake horsepower and is also less than the PTO horsepower. For example, a 78hp tractor might have a drawbar power of only 60hp available for pulling a trailer or implement, and this is decreased even more when you take into account ground resistance to the wheels. Check the tractor handbook for its nominal drawbar power when choosing trailers. (A reminder: 1hp in theory represents the capacity to move a load weighing 330 pounds a distance of a hundred feet in a minute, or a weight of 33,000 pounds a distance of one foot in a minute, and is the equivalent of 0.75 kilowatts.)

Towing a trailer, or any other trailed implement for that matter, requires some skill in manoeuvring round corners. If you are harrowing, for example, a typical beginner's mistake is to turn too sharply at the headland on a slight slope and end up with the harrow climbing onto one of the tractor's rear wheels. With trailers, the greatest skill lies in reversing round a corner — a common manoeuvre in the yard, especially when unloading. Trailers never quite seem to go in the direction you expect.

If a trailer is taken on to a public road, you need a legally acceptable braking system, proper lights in poor visibility or at night, and (with new trailers) direction indicators.

Self-propelled machinery

If your main requirement is tillage on a small scale, or the control of grass in a small paddock or orchard, take a look at the considerable range of self-propelled, pedestrian operated machines and implements designed for cultivating large gardens and horticultural enterprises. On a five-acre holding in Hampshire, for example, a couple grew excellent fodder crops of kale and mangolds for their four cows, four heifers and ten calves by manuring the ground thoroughly (with the courtesy of the bullock shed), then sowing it by means of a push seed-drill, followed by an empty wheelbarrow because its tyre was ideal for rolling in the seed!

A little more sophisticated are what some describe as 'two-wheeled tractors'. These cultivators have petrol or diesel engines ranging from perhaps 5hp to 14hp or more in the larger models, with powered wheels, several gears, independent PTO and a range of implements including cultivators, rotary hoes, bottom ploughs, single ploughs, reversible ploughs, ridgers, scythe cutter bars (some up to almost 1.3m in width), lawn mowers, rotary mowers, snow throwers, dozer blades, clipper/shredders, fertiliser spreaders, sprayers, power brushes, log splitters and so on. Some can tow a very small horticultural trailer, which effectively turns the machine into a little ride-on. Many a smallholder cuts hay with an aged and irreplaceable Allen motor scythe or its modern foreign-made equivalent.

Chainsaws

Chainsaws should be treated with great respect: if they can cut down trees, they can certainly slice through flesh. By law, employees should wear a safety helmet, ear muffs, eye goggles, safety boots and protective gloves and leggings, and you should at least seek the chainsaw manufacturer's advice about using and caring for the implement. Even better, ask your nearest agricultural college or forestry commission office about instruction courses. Chainsaws are not toys: the engine speed when the machine is cutting is 7,000–10,000 rpm.

The typical farm chainsaw has a two-stroke single-cylinder petrol engine of perhaps 2.8–4.8hp (2.1–3.6kW) and a chain guide bar of somewhere between 38 and 53cm long. Ensure that the tension of the chain is correct by pulling it fully round the guide bar in the normal running direction, using one gloved hand with a pulling action. In particular, make sure it is not so loose that the chain comes off. Keep the chain blades sharp` enough to throw out wood chips rather than a lot of sawdust and keep the chain well lubricated (check the oil reservoir frequently). Maintenance should be a priority and you should always check that external nuts and screws are secure before use and that the chain brake and on/off switch are functioning.

For a cold start: put the saw on the ground with your booted foot on the rear handle plate. Put a hand on the front handle; engage half throttle stop, pull out the choke and switch on; pull the starter cord firmly. If the machine is already warm, you will not need to use the choke or half throttle stop.

There is now a kit on the market which can convert your chainsaw into a portable winch — but it costs a thousand pounds!

Milking machines

It is possible to buy milking machines for only a couple of animals: it is hardly cost-effective, but at least you can more readily persuade a stand-in to do the milking if you cannot do it yourself. Make sure that you do not overmilk with a machine or you could cause damage to the udder.

Machines can speed up milking time if you are not a good handmilker; they can also enable two animals (or more) to be milked simultaneously and they transfer the milk straight from the teat to an enclosed container so that, as long as all the equipment (including the teat) is scrupulously clean, the risk of contamination is greatly reduced. However, the machine can also be a haven

for bacteria if hygiene is skimped, and it must be properly maintained if it is to be both efficient and kind to the udder. There is the drawback that the machine distances you from the udder: if you are handmilking you will spot problems before they become so.

In essence, a milking machine draws milk from the teat by means of a pulsating mechanism which (like the hand) alternately creates and releases pressure, through the medium of a rubber-lined cup for each teat at perhaps 60 cycles per minute. The milk is usually then conveyed away from the teat by vacuum. The teat cups and the 'claw' which holds them are known jointly as the cluster, which has a single tube leading away from it into the milk collection system. Milking machines can be powered by mains electricity, battery or petrol, and no doubt someone is working on water-powered, solar-powered or wind-driven models.

The most basic machines, which could be worth investing in if you milk, say, half a dozen animals or more, are mobile vacuum pumps with one or two enclosed milk receptacles and clusters. The capacity of the receptacle is of course quite low — up to about 25 litres — which means it needs to be emptied into a larger container at intervals. Its mobility is hampered by the weight of its engine and some models have trolleys so that they can be trundled out to the field.

The portable milking bail is in effect a wheeled shed fully fitted with milking machinery: you take the parlour to the animals rather than inviting them into the yard.

Some of the portable systems have stainless steel receptacles but others have graduated transparent jars so that you can check each animal's yield as you milk. Some allow you to alter vacuum pressures and fit different clusters so that you can milk different species of livestock — cows, nanny goats, ewes or whatever you wish. Portable systems can also be linked to vacuum lines fixed permanently in a cowshed, though the containers still need to be emptied by hand and need to be handwashed as well, whereas the type of milking system used by commercial herds or flocks has a permanent pipeline to convey the milk to a bulk container and built-in systems for washing out all the equipment after milking.

Whatever the milking system, it must be maintained in good condition as well as being kept very clean. In particular, make sure that the rubber teat cups do not cause discomfort to the animal and that the pulsation rate is appropriate.

Sources

With the increasing interest in smallholding, which began to develop again with the self-sufficiency movement in the early 1970s after a lapse since the 1950s, there are more and more suppliers catering for the needs of those who operate on a small scale and who might not be able to find what they need through normal agricultural suppliers. The Addresses section lists some of the smallholding magazines, which are excellent sources of information and advertisements. It also lists some of the smallholders' suppliers, whose illustrated catalogues give some idea of the range of manufactured articles available and might inspire you to make some of your own. Have fun!

VI Alternative Energy

The main energy sources used by farmers and smallholders today are petrochemicals and electricity, both of which were unknown to earlier generations, who relied on renewable on-farm resources — basically human and animal muscles or, in suitable places and for specific applications, power harnessed from water, wind or the burning of wood and charcoal. Now, with non-renewable resources becoming depleted, some of those involved in agriculture are taking a look at alternative energy sources.

Animal power

It is only in the most developed countries that we have lost touch with working animals. Much of the world still relies on them for cultivations, draught power and personal transport but in the West we have what the Indian author H. R. Arakeri calls 'the other extreme of animal-less farming'. As Arakeri puts it: 'Biological power dominates in the developing countries, machine power dominates in the developed countries.' Seventy years ago there were 24 million working horses and mules in the United States where before the First World War a quarter of agricultural land was apparently devoted to feeding working animals. In India there are even now perhaps 80 million working cattle and water buffalo, mainly existing on miserably low rations, and there is also a very high level of human labour — men, women and children — and only two million tractors.

Farm animals have at least one major advantage over tractors: they can reproduce. They can also renew their own energy, largely by eating the grassland plants which humans are unable to digest — and they maintain the holding's energy cycle by returning manure to the ground to keep it fertile. They give more than muscle power: we drink their milk, eat their offspring, spin their fibre and tan their hides, and in parts of the world where firewood is in short supply animal dung is essential as fuel. And they are mammals, like we are: it is much more satisfying to work with a mammal than a machine. There is no warmth to a tractor, no spirit, no *life*.

Yes, animals work more slowly than tractors and, yes, as living creatures they require more consideration than machines, but they are far cheaper to buy and replace and they are so much more verstaile, not only in being able to go where a tractor cannot but also in their ability to give such a variety of essential poroduce. You cannot get milk out of a tractor: a tractor is entirely a consumer, not a producer.

Worldwide, the most common working animals are cattle (including water buffalo) and they always have been. Even in this country, oxen were the major source of farm power for many centuries; they did not begin to be supplanted by working horses on the farm until the 18th century (and more comprehensively towards the end of the 19th), and horses, in their turn were not seriously challenged by machines until the Second World War. During the war, tractors were regarded as merely supplementary to horses, but after the war they began to oust them quite rapidly.

There is a very gentle revival of interest in working horses in Britain today, with a few farmers making serious use of them, and in major forestry countries (such as Sweden) horses are valued for their ability to work where machines fear to tread. One or two people are toying with the idea of training oxen for work, too, but it is highly unlikely

Smallholder's horse earning its keep by bringing hay to livestock.

that Britain will ever use them again to the extent that they are employed in Asia and Africa, where they are vital to local economies.

There are other possibilities. Donkeys have their limitations, mainly because they are small, but mules can be huge and offer a great deal of stamina and strength to those who understand their ways and are prepared to be patient with them. However, mules cannot reproduce as they are hybrids, the offspring of jack asses mated to mares (the stallion/jenny cross is a hinny). Mules and donkeys are particularly useful for routine work: they are happy enough to plod a repetitive route, to the extent that a train of mules hardly needs the presence of a human minder at all. They are best suited as pack animals but after the First World War those who had become familiar with Army mules used them on the farm and preferred them to horses for ploughing.

Goats can be trained to pull very light carts and often rather enjoy having a 'job'. Pigs, too, are extremely intelligent and have been used in the past for some fairly unlikely work, including being harnessed to small carriers, hunting for truffles, 'racing' and, in all seriousness, retrieving for game-keepers. There was a retrieving ewe on the Scottish hills in the 19th century, with an unfortunate and unlikely habit of eating the gamebirds she caught, and there is today a pet ewe on a Cumbrian smallholding trained

to the harness: she has a custom-made cart in which she willingly carries grass-cuttings around the place.

Dogs were quite widely used in the 19th century as draught animals and there were many dog teams drawing small cartfuls of produce to market, for example fish from the south coast to Billingsgate, until too many people complained of the loud barking and the number of dogfights caused by the reactions of local curs through whose territory the teams passed.

Today the serious choice for farmwork lies between the ox and the horse. The main problem is not so much the training as finding appropriate implements but you could talk to the curator of a nearby working open-air museum or contact the Shire Horse Society, who are taking the future of the working horse very seriously and can give a great deal of good, practical advice to those who have a sensible interest. For ideas on equipment suitable for working oxen, look to the developing countries. You need a wellbuilt breed with more shoulder than rump: originally (and still to some extent in a few European countries) cattle were triple-purpose, expected to work and produce milk, and then to be eaten when they were no longer fit for work, but we have specialised for several generations and have lost the true working oxen conformation. The major draught breeds of the past were

144

big animals like the Longhorn or reds such as the Sussex, Devon and Hereford, but the Butser Iron Age Farm in Hampshire has been successfully putting Dexters to the plough — including the cows.

Horses were still used on many smaller farms after the Second World War and even in the fifties the quality of Britain's draught horses was as renowned as that of her hunters and ponies. The most common farm breeds were Shire, Clydesdale, Suffolk Punch and Percheron (originally a French breed) and a lot of perfectly good mongrels as well. The first two were heavy draughts for large-scale farmers, whereas small farmers needed horses with good strength and stamina but light enough to trot and not too demanding for fodder: Punches and Percherons suited them well. I still meet men who used to work horses, perhaps when they were boys or in their first farm post, and they nearly all remember them with great affection, humour and pride.

The basic equipment for a small farm would have included a single-furrow plough, a three-leaved set of spiked harrows, a horse-roller and a grubber or tine-harrows; drills, reapers and binders were hired or employed when required. Other implements might include a set of discs for working heavy or very 'dirty' land, a horse-hoe for roots or market garden crops, a fertiliser and lime distributor — and of course all sorts of wains, wagons or carts.

Biogas

This is a byproduct of livestock production. In several countries, including the Netherlands, Germany and Ireland, there are serious practical enterprises in which the gas produced by slurry and manure is harnessed as a source of energy. The idea is far from original: biogas from organic waste has been recognised and used for many years, especially in developing countries with warmer climates than ours. Biogas is up to 69 per cent methane and up to 35 per cent carbon dioxide, with traces of other gases, and it has a reasonably high calorific value. If it is drawn off for heating or to generate power, there is the additional benefit of reducing

the smelliness of untreated manure from something like 60 million tonnes of excreta produced by housed livestock in the UK.

The main problems in biogas production have been keeping the slurry at 35°C in the digester (by burning some of the gas produced) and storing the gas for later use. Another problem is that methane is itself a 'greenhouse' gas, even more efficient than carbon dioxide at trapping solar heat in the atmosphere, and there could be serious consequences if surplus biogas is simply vented rather than utilised.

Straw

In some parts of the country straw is regarded as a waste product and its disposal a nuisance, because it is too bulky to be transported economically to livestock enterprises and anyway many of the latter no longer use bedding straw. So it is either chopped and ploughed back into the land (which can be good) or, until recently, burned in the field. However, it could more profitably be burned as fuel in special straw-fired boilers or converted into compressed straw briquettes for use on domestic open fires and kitchen ranges. (The name can be misleading: I once visited a farm where such briquettes were being produced by a co-operative but which specialised in Jersey cow cream and soft fruit. It was February, and the elderly cowman who heard my request looked at me pityingly. 'We don't grow no strawb'rries in Feb'ry,' he said.)

Wind and water

'Steam, horse, and water power, have been variously used for driving stationary machinery. The two former require the expenditure of fuel or feed, and the latter does not exist on many farms, and can be only occasionally used. But there is another, and universal power — found on every part of every single farm in the world — and sweeping over all with a strength of thousands of horses — which has been very little used for farm purposes. This is wind.' [*The American Agriculturist*, 1873] A commercial windfarm is planned for Cornwall, generating enough electricity for

Wind-powered drainage mill, originally to drain brick-clay pits; now purely decorative on its new site at the Weald and Downland Open Air Museum in Sussex.

2,000 houses from ten turbines, each 24m tall. To produce the same amount of electricity from coal would require 4,000t of the irreplaceable raw material and its burning would produce 10,000t of carbon dioxide.

A Leicestershire farmer is less ambitious but is self-sufficient in farm power generated by two 13m-tall wind turbine towers which produce 14kW/hour on a good day with a steady wind at 25mph. He also has the back-up of a set of solar generators (6kW/hour) and a propane-powered generator (15kW/hour). He stores his surplus electricity in batteries and sells what he does not use.

Turbines are very expensive to install, and obtaining planning permission for them can be a nightmare, but there are simpler devices which might be windpowered — for fun if not for any great practical benefit. Little things, like windmills to drive butter churns perhaps . . . More seriously, windmills played an important role in helping to drain agricultural land in the past or to irrigate fields and supply livestock with water. They have been used to thresh corn as well as mill it, or to hoist hay and straw, or grind and chop feed, or saw and plane wood, indeed to run machinery of all kinds, including some in the farm workshop. The problem, of course, is that the mill stops when the wind stops.

When available, water is perhaps a more reliable source of power than wind: it is easier to control. There is a real practical possibility of generating your own electricity from water if you can work out how to construct a system at less than an astronomical outlay. The use of falling water as a source of power goes back a long, long way — certainly to at least 600BC in the Far East — and it developed rapidly in ancient Rome, whence it became widespread throughout the Roman empire. A detailed water-wheel was described by Vitruvius in *De architectura* within a few decades of the birth of Christ, and this wondrous machine relieved women of the endless task of handmilling grain. However, the poets wondered what all the women would *do* with so much new time on their hands and the Greek poet Antipater of Thessalonia bade them to 'sleep on, though the crowing cock announce the break of day'. The watermill became indispensible to the household, even though its output was no more than half a horsepower, or 300–400 watts.

Human power

In the early days of agriculture, the only source of energy for working the land was human musclepower. Ever since the first people found ways of harnessing animal power and the powers of nature, farmers have sought to become the directors of power (from whatever source) rather than expending their own bodies' energy. However, it is still possible, even if not 'efficient', to carry out any farming operation by hand, given enough hands and enough time. Is it not strange that so many people in this country today look to sport in order to burn off their excess energy? When jogging first became a national occupation in the 1970s, a dairy farmer remarked to me that she could find endless 'exercise' for all those joggers, right there on her farm — mucking out, perhaps, or humping bales and feedbags. Some people will even pay to work on your smallholding: they appreciate how lucky you are to be in contact with the realities of mud and muck, plants and animals — life!

Hmm. *Every* day?

Appendix 1

Soil sampling chart

1. Does it form a ball when moist?
   Easily: ➤ 3.
   With care: Loamy Sand
   No: Sand

2. If you leave a ball to dry and then press it, does it shatter easily?
   Yes: Probably easy-to-work Medium Loam
   No: Probably heavy with high Clay content

3. If you press a moistened ball between finger and thumb, does it:
   Flatten: ➤ 4.
   Break up: Sandy Loam

4. If you moisten it a little more, can you roll it into a 'worm' about 5 mm thick?
   Yes: ➤ 5.
   No: Loamy Sand

5. If you moisten it even more, can you roll it into a thin 'worm' about 2 mm thick?
   Yes: ➤ 6.
   No: Sandy Loam

6. Can you bend the thin worm into a horseshoe around the side of your hand without cracking it?
   Yes: ➤ 8.
   No: ➤ 7.

7. Moisten it again and remould it. What does it feel like?
   Smooth and pasty: Silt Loam
   Rough and abrasive: Sandy Silt Loam

8. Can you make a ring 25 mm in diameter from the thin worm without cracking it?
   Yes: ➤ 10.
   No: ➤ 9.

9. Moisten it again and remould it. What does it feel like:
   Very gritty: Sandy Clay Loam
   Moderately rough: Clay Loam
   Doughy: Silt Clay Loam

10. Remould it without wetting. Can you make a polished surface by rubbing with your thumb?
   High polish like wax with only a few noticeable particles: ➤ 11.
   High polish but gritty particles still very noticeable: Sandy Clay
   No polish: ➤ 9.

11. Wet the sample thoroughly. How strongly does it stick your fingers together?
   Very: Clay
   Moderately: Silty Clay

Appendix 2

Soil Characteristics

Clay soils:

Sticky when wet. Hold more water: useful in dry weather but lie wet in winter, therefore liable to be poached (trampled by livestock). Slow to warm up in spring. Fairly rich in potash, deficient in phosphates. Structure can be improved by liming. Do not try to work in spring if wet: it will puddle and clod. Deep cracks in dry spells. Need much more power to cultivate/plough. Autumn digging or ploughing essential for spring tilth (let frosts attack clods). Good drainage essential, e.g. ridge-and-furrow ploughing or mole drains. Add OM to make it easier to work. Grow winter wheat, winter beans, mangolds, cabbages, sugarbeet, potatoes, or put down to permanent grass to avoid cultivation problems but keep livestock off in winter.

Sandy soils:

'Light' for easy cultivation. Can be worked any time, even if wet. Free-drainage unless impervious underlayer. High proportion of sand, very little clay. Warms early in spring but low water rentention, low in nutrients, fertilisers are easily leached out. Lime carefully, little and often. OM (especially FYM) very useful, also irrigation. Can have problems of erosion by wind: use shelterbelts or practise claying. Wide crop range possible but yields depend on irrigation and fertilising. Market garden produce, rye, carrots, sugarbeet, lucerne, lupins, barley, potatoes, peas.

Loams:

Heavy/clay, medium or light/sandy. Advantages of both extremes without the disadvantages. Easily worked (but keep off when wet). Simple drainage. Best all-round soil for cropping: naturally fertile, good for any crop if deep enough, consistent yields. Arable, grass, or mixed. Cereals, potatoes, sugarbeet; grazing leys, bulk winter foods for livestock.

Calcareous soils:

Derived from chalk and limestone rocks, 5–50 per cent calcium carbonate. 8cm–1m deep; deeper soils usually more fertile. Clay and chalk content determine stickiness — usually loamy. Often contain flints. Free-draining except on deepish clay subsoils. Deficient in P and K but do not usually need liming. OM beneficial but breaks down too quickly. Barley, wheat, roots, leys, kale.

Silts:

Main problem is bad drainage. Lime is not helpful. Difficult to create easily worked structure. Deep-rooted crops (e.g. lucerne) for several years help to open subsoil and improve drainage. Arable very difficult: best left as permanent grass. Mostly found in Lower Weald.

Peats and peaty soils:

Peaty soils 20–25 per cent OM, peats 50–90 per cent. Acid or peatbog peats and peaty soils in waterlogged areas from dead plant matter: break down easily when reclaimed and release nutrients, especially N, but very low in P and K. Need good drainage — deep ditches and deep ploughing — and lots of lime to neutralise acidity. Lots of FYM in first year for crops like potatoes, then put down to good grass and clover but beware of poaching. Potatoes and oats are best but can cultivate most arable crops.

Black Fen soils:

Fenland 'silts' are alluvial and fairly easy to work. Very fertile, very high levels of OM. Reclaimed by building sea-walls and putting in deep drainage. Dry, sooty black, friable, breaks down readily, easily windblown if not clayed. Rich in N but very poor in P and K and trace elements (manganese, copper etc.). Limited leys. Intensive arable, all sorts of crops — wheat, potatoes, sugarbeet, also market gardening.

Appendix 3

Soil acidity: pH values for different crops

Crops will tolerate lower pH values than those they prefer, but below these tolerances their growth will be poor.

CROP	pH TOLERANCE
Legumes	
Lucerne	6.2
Sainfoin	6.2
Trefoil	6.1
Vetches	5.9
Alsike clover	5.7
White clover	5.6
Wild white clover	4.7
Beans/peas	
Beans	6.0
Peas	5.9
Cereals and Grasses	
Barley	5.9
Maize	5.6
Wheat	5.6
Oats	5.3
Cocksfoot and Timothy	5.3
Rye	4.9
Fescues and Ryegrasses	4.7

CROP	pH TOLERANCE
Roots	
Sugarbeet and Beetroot	5.9
Mangolds	5.8
Carrots	5.7
Swedes, Turnips and Parsnips	5.4
Potatoes	4.9
Brassicas	
Brussels sprouts	5.7
Forage rape	5.6
Cauliflower	5.6
Kale and Cabbage	5.4
Other crops	
Mint	6.6
Celery	6.3
Lettuce	6.1
Asparagus	5.9
Spinach	5.8
Onions	5.7
Cucumber	5.5
Linseed and Mustard	5.4
Chicory, Parsley, Tomato	5.1

Appendix 4

Manure

(A) Daily production of dung and urine

ANIMALS	AV. BODYWEIGHT (kg)	DUNG+URINE (litres/day)
Dairy cow	500	41–45
Two year old beef bullock	400	27
One year old bullock	220	15
Pigs (depending on diet)	50	4–7
Pigs on whey/swill	50	14
Sow and litter (to three weeks old)	170	15
100 laying hens		11–14

(B) Nutrients available to crops (manure spread in spring*)

*(N will be lost if manure is spread in autumn or winter. Because of severe losses from leaching, if the amount of N available from spring-spread manure is taken as 100, the equivalent when spread in autumn = 0–20; early winter = 30–50; late winter = 60–90.)

SOURCE	% DRY MATTER	% OF FRESH WEIGHT			AVAILABLE TO CROP (kg/t or kg/cu.m)		
		N	P	K	N	P	K
Cattle: FYM	25	0.6	0.3	0.7	1.5	2.0	4.0
Undiluted slurry	10	0.5	0.2	0.5	2.5	1.0	4.5
Pigs: FYM	25	0.6	0.6	0.4	1.5	4.0	2.5
Undiluted slurry	Up to 10	0.6	0.4	0.3	4.0	2.0	2.7
Poultry: Deeplitter	70	1.7	1.8	1.3	10.0	11.0	10.0
Undiluted slurry	25	1.4	1.1	0.6	9.1	5.5	5.4
Straw compost	25–30	0.4	0.2	0.3			
Fresh seaweed	20	0.2	0.1	1.2			
Dried sewage sludge	60–90	2.0	3.0	0.5			

$(P=P_2O_5, K=K_2O)$

Thus 10 tons of FYM might produce the following:

Cattle:	15kg N	20kg P	40kg K
Pigs:	15kg N	40kg P	25kg K
Poultry:	100kg N	110kg P	100kg K

Appendix 5

Field crops

Cereals

WHEAT	Durum for pasta, milling wheats, livestock feed; straw for animal litter (harder and less absorbent than barley straw) or thatch.
BARLEY	Livestock feed, or malting barley; straw as cattle feed or litter.
OATS	Livestock feed, a little for breakfast cereal etc.; straw as cattle/sheep feed.
RYE	Livestock feed or forage crop seed.

Beans and peas

FIELD BEANS	Livestock feed and N fixation.
GREEN BEANS AND PEAS	Human consumption or livestock feed.

Oilseeds

OILSEED RAPE	Oil.
LINSEED/FLAX	Same species: linseed for oil, flax for fibre.

Forage and roots

The following can be fed to livestock (some are also or primarily grown as cash crops):

POTATOES	Main cash crop; surplus to livestock.
SUGAR BEET	Grown on contract with British Sugar under quota; wilted tops for livestock feeding or silage.
FODDER BEET	Bulk feed for cattle and sheep.
MANGELS	Less valuable bulk feed than fodder beet — must be ripened before being fed (store in clamp).
TURNIPS/SWEDES	Swedes higher DM and feed value, will store for winter feeding. Turnips often left in ground for sheep to graze but swedes lifted and clamped. Both for cattle as well as sheep feeding. STUBBLE TURNIPS more leaf than root, quick to grow, sown in cereal stubble after harvest for sheep folding.
OTHER ROOTS	Surplus as animal feed locally: carrots, beetroot, parsnip (the latter to pigs).

Forage

FORAGE RAPE	Quick-growing good protein-rich feed, similar to tops of turnip/swede —grown alone or with kale, turnips, ryegrass etc., or undersown with cereals for autumn grazing, especially sheep in west and north.
KALE	Huge yields, successful forage crop, cheap and easy to grow, leaf better nutrition than stem, several types for different purposes — graze, cut-and-cart (mower or forage harvester). Drumhead cattle cabbage similar value but handcut.
MAIZE	Whole-crop silage, game cover.

Appendix 6

Grasses

The major pasture and ley grasses are SHORT-DURATION RYEGRASSES (for example, Italian ryegrass with a useful life of two years or so) and PERENNIAL RYEGRASSES (major longterm constituent, several varieties), both of which can produce heavy crops on good soils and respond well to N fertilisers, and MEADOW FESCUE, COCKSFOOT and TIMOTHY. None of these major species are hairy, and all grow in tufts. Other minor species in permanent pasture are used as *bottom grasses* to thicken the base of the sward. There are also many *weed grasses*, usually unpalatable.

Identification

	ITALIAN RYEGRASS	PERENNIAL RYEGRASS	MEADOW FESCUE	COCKSFOOT	TIMOTHY
LEAF SHEATH	Split	Split or entire	Split	Entire, split later	Split
BASE COLOUR	Pinkish	Pinkish	Pinkish	Light	Pale brown. May be swollen
LEAF IN SHOOT	Rolled	Folded	Rolled	Folded	Rolled
BLADE WIDTH	Broad	Narrow	Narrow	Broad	Broad
BLADE MARGINS	Smooth	Smooth	Rough	Rough	Smooth
BLADE COLOUR	Dark Green	Dark Green	Lighter Green	Light Green	Light Green
UNDERSIDE	Shiny	Shiny	Shiny	Dull	Dull
LIGULE	Blunt	Blunt, small, clasps stem	Blunt, small, greenish white	Long, transparent	Prominent, membranous
AURICLES	Medium, spreading	Small	Small, narrow, spreading	Absent	Absent
TEXTURE	Smooth	Smooth	Smooth	Rough	Smooth
FLOWERS	Panicle	Panicle	Panicle	Panicle	Spike

Weed grasses

BENT (AGROSTIS)

Very common, forms good undermat but late, with low yield and not particularly palatable. Stolons rather than tufted — stems run over soil surface. Smooth texture, long narrow leaf.

YORKSHIRE FOG

Extremely unpalatable except when very young. Sign of acidity. Soft and hairy, white base, light colour.

COUCH (TWITCH)

Invasive arable weed, difficult to eradicate. Rhizomes and creeping stems. As bad as WILD OATS and BLACKGRASS.

Properties

	ITALIAN RYEGRASS	PERENNIAL RYEGRASS	MEADOW FESCUE	COCKSFOOT	TIMOTHY
ESTABLISHMENT	Very quick	Quick	Slow	Quick	Fairly quick
SEASON	Early. Heavy spring yields	Very early to very late varieties. Good yields in spring, early summer or autumn	Fairly early once established, also late varieties	Fairly early to late varieties. High yields	Not very early to late varieties. Less productive
SOILS	Best on fertile, responds to N	Best on fertile, responds to N		Less fertile, light, low rainfall	Best on good but not very light dry
DIGESTIBILITY	High	High	High	Not as high	Not as high
PALATABILITY	Good but stemmy		Very good	Needs heavy stocking to avoid becoming coarse and unpalatable	Very good
HARDINESS	Winter hardiness improved if surplus autumn growth removed	Hard-wearing, stays green in winter but grows very little in July-August	Stays green in winter, grows well in autumn too; often mixed with Timothy	Strong, very deep rooting so very drought resistant and grows well in summer to counterbalance ryegrass	Winter hardy; not so strong; not good competitor with IRG or Cocksfoot; goes on growing in summer; stays green in winter

Bottom grasses

ROUGH-STALKED MEADOW GRASS
Well liked and palatable. Common; prefers moister soils. Useful in older leys when clover dies out.

SMOOTH-STALKED MEADOW GRASS
Well liked and palatable. Withstands drier conditions.

SMALL FESCUES
Creeping lawn grasses. RED FESCUE useful on marginal land.

TALL FESCUE
Very hardy and very early. Useful once established, can be grazed during winter, but not very productive. MEADOW FOXTAIL is another very early bottom grass.

CRESTED DOGSTAIL
Small. Wiry flowerstem — not very palatable.

SWEET VERNAL GRASS
Deceptively sweet-smelling as hay — bitter tasting.

153

Appendix 7

Pasture plants

(A) Poisonous

(* = more dangerous, and some remain so even when dried in hay) Note that many of the following plants are unpalatable and will not be eaten anyway but some become addictive. Note also that many are excellent herbal remedies or tonics in small quantities, only becoming dangerous if large quantities are eaten.

Acorns

Ash keys

*Belladonna family

Box

*Bracken

Broomrape

*Buckthorn

Buckwheat

Bulbs, corms, rhizomes

Charlock family

*Cowbane

*Flax

Fodderbeet/kale in excess

*Foxglove

Hemlock

*Horsetail

Houndstongue

Hypericum

Ivy

*Lily of the valley

*Lupin

*Mangels, fresh

Meadow saffron

Mistletoe berries

*Pink family

*Poppy family

Potatoes, green, or stem/leaves

Privet

*Ragwort

*Ranunculus family

Rhododendron

Sedum

Sorrel

Spindle

Spurges and mercuries

Sugarbeet tops, unwilted

Tomato stems/leaves

Tobacco

*White bryony

*Yew

(B) Plants affecting milk

(Some of the plants which taint milk are useful herbal remedies)

PLANT	INCREASES MILK YIELD	INCREASES BUTTER FAT	TAINTS MILK	USEFUL MILK CURDLER	PROBLEMS FOR BUTTER MAKING	PROBLEMS FOR CHEESE MAKING
Anise	*		*			
Balm	*					
Bedstraw				*		
Borage	*					
Buckwheat		*				
Buttercup		*	*			
Butterwort				*		
Chamomile			*			
Carrot		*				
Chervil	*	*				
Clover	*					
Cow wheat			*			
Elder blossom		*				
Fennel	*		*			
Fool's parlsey			*			
Garlic/onion			*			
Hedge mustard			*			
Ivy			*			
Knotgrass			*			
Knotweed			*			
Linseed		*				
Maize		*				
Marigold		*				
Marshmallow	*					
Marsh marigold			*			
Melilot, Blue	*			*		
Milkwort	*					
Mint			*		*	*
Nettles				*		
Oats		*				
Ox-eye daisy			*			
Pennycress			*			
Pine kernels	*					
Sage	*		*			
Sorrel			*	*	*	
Sow thistle	*					
Sugarbeet top/pulp in excess			*			
Sunflower seed	*					
Tansy			*			
Turnips			*			
Watercress			*			
Waterparsnip			*			
Wild radish			*			
Wood sorrel					*	
Wormwood			*			
Yarrow			*			

Metric/Imperial conversions

IMPERIAL	:	METRIC	METRIC	:	IMPERIAL	(APPROXIMATIONS)
1 inch	=	2.54 cm	1 mm	=	0.04 in	(inch × 10/4 = cm)
1 foot	=	0.30 m	1 cm	=	0.39 in	(foot × 3/10 = metres)
1 yard	=	0.91 m	1 m	=	1.09 yd	(yard × 9/10 = metres)
1 mile	=	1.61 km	1 km	=	0.62 mi	
1 sq.in	=	6.45 cm^2	1 cm^2	=	0.16 sq.in	
1 sq.ft	=	0.09 m^2	1 m^2	=	10.8 sq.ft	(sq.ft × 1/11 = m^2)
1 sq.yd	=	0.86 m^2	1 m^2	=	1.20 sq.yd	(sq.yd × 5/6 = m^2)
1 acre	=	0.405 ha	1 ha	=	2.47 acres	(acre × 4/10 = hectares)
1 fl.oz	=	28.4 ml	1 ml	=	0.035 fl.oz	
1 pint	=	0.57 l	1 l	=	1.76 pt	(pint × 4/7 = litres)
1 gallon	=	4.55 l	1 l	=	0.22 gal	(gallon × 9/2 = litres)
1 ounce	=	28.35 g	1 g	=	0.035 oz	
1 pound	=	0.45 kg	1 kg	=	2.20 lb	(pound × 9/20 = kg)
1 cwt	=	50.8 kg				(cwt × 50 = kg)
1 ton	=	1.016 t	1 t	=	0.984 tons	
1 horsepower	=	0.75 kilowatts	1 kW	=	1.34 hp	(hp × 3/4 = kW)

Addresses

Magazines

APPROPRIATE TECHNOLOGY
Intermediate Technology Publications, 103–105 Southampton Row, London WC1B 4HH.

GREEN PAGES
Directory (free to farmers, or £10.75 a copy) listing more than 75,000 agricultural suppliers, services and advisors, 84A Turnham Green Terrace, London W4 1QN.

HOME FARM
Broad Leys Publishing Co., Buriton House, Station Road, Newport, Saffron Walden, Essex CB11 3PZ.

SMALLHOLDER
Smallholder Publications Ltd., High Street, Stoke Ferry, King's Lynn, Norfolk PE33 9SF.

S.F.A. NEWS
Small Farmers Association, PO Box 6, Ludlow, Salop SY8 1ZZ.

General

AGRICULTURAL TRAINING BOARD
Bourne House, 32–34 Beckenham Road, Beckenham, Kent BR3 4PB.

CEMENT AND CONCRETE ASSOCIATION
Wexham Springs, Slough, Bucks SL3 6PL.

FARM AND RURAL BUILDINGS CENTRE
National Agricultural Centre, Stoneleigh, Warwickshire OV8 2LG (publish *Farm Building and Equipment Directory*).

FORESTRY COMMISION
231 Corstorphine Road, Edinburgh.

NATIONAL HEDGELAYING SOCIETY
17 Sandhills Road, Barnt Green, Birmingham.

ROYAL AGRICULTURAL SOCIETY OF ENGLAND
National Agricultural Centre, Stoneleigh, Kenilworth, Warwickshire CV8 2LG.

SHIRE HORSE SOCIETY
East of England Showground, Peterborough PE2 0XE.

SOIL ASSOCIATION
86/88 Colston Street, Bristol BS1 5BB.

Suppliers

General

DALTON SUPPLIES LTD.
Nettlebed, Henley on Thames, Oxfordshire.

LINCOLNSHIRE SMALLHOLDERS SUPPLIES LTD.
Thorpe Fendykes, Wainfleet, Skegness, Lincs PE24 4QH.

NET-TEX AGRICULTURAL LTD.
8 Milton Road, Gravesend, Kent DA12 2RE.

SMALLHOLDING AND FARM SUPPLY CO.
Gerard Street, Heeley, Sheffield S8 9SJ.

SMALLHOLDING SUPPLIES
Pikes Farmhouse, East Pennard, Shepton Mallet, Somerset BA4 6RR.

S.P.R. POULTRY AND SELF-SUFFICENCY CENTRE
Greenfields Farm, Fontwell Avenue, Eastergate, Chichester, West Sussex (office and shop at Barnham Station, Bognor Regis).

Buildings

F.R.I. (polytunnels etc.)
College House, Penstrowed, Newtown, Powys SY17 5SG.

NEWBRIDGE FARM PRODUCTS
(sectional timber, for smallholders)
Newbridge Farm, Aylton, Ledbury, Herefordshire.

POLYBUILD (polypens)
Unit 9C, Tewkesbury Industrial Centre, Delta Drive, Tewkesbury, Gloucestershire GL20 8HB.

Fencing

DRIVALL LTD.
   Narrow Lane, Halesowen, West Midlands B62 9PA.

FIELDGUARD LTD.
   Grove Heath Farm, Ripley, Woking, Surrey GU23 6ES.

JACKSONS FENCING
   273 Stowting Common, Ashford, Kent.

Machinery/Implements

ATCO
   The DMP Building, The Terrace, Sunninghill, Ascot, Berkshire SL5 9NH.

B.C.S (two-wheel tractors)
   Tracmaster, Burgess Hill, West Sussex RH15 9ZA.

DUFFIELDS LTD. (ATV attachments and distributors of Honda ATVs)
   Brunel Road, Churchfields, Salisbury, Wiltshire SP2 7PU.

HERON SUZUKI PLC (ATVs)
   PO Box 154, Tunbridge Wells, Kent TN1 1JR.

HONDA U.K. LTD. (ATVs)
   Power Road, Chiswick, London W4 5YT.

KAWASAKI MOTORS (U.K.) LTD. (ATVs)
   1 Dukes Meadow, Millboard Road, Bourne End, Buckinghamshire SL8 5XF.

LOGIC ATV-EQUIP (ATV attachments)
   Foundry Industrial Estate, Bridge End, Hexham, Northumberland NE46 4JL.
      and
   Unit 2, Hazleton Industrial Estate, Hazelton, Cheltenham, Gloucestershire GL54 4DX.

MITSUI MACHINERY SALES (UK) LTD. (Yamaha ATVs)
   Oakcroft Road, Chessington, Surrey KT9 1SA.

RAFFERTY NEWMAN (distributors of wide range of ATVs, ATV attachments and compact tractors)
   Unit 5, Amey Industrial Estate, Petersfield, Hampshire GU32 3AN.

S.E.P. U.K. (two-wheel tractors)
   H.G.B. Tool & Plant, 69–79 Park Way, Ruislip Manor.

STIHL LTD. (chainsaws — useful safety manual)
   Goldsworth Park Industrial Estate, Woking, Surrey GU21 3BA.

Secondhand

BURGESS
   (More than fifty branches nationwide for used machinery — see local telephone directory or contact the Stafford office, 0785 223131).

DAVID AVES AGRICULTURAL ENGINEERS (small milking machines)
   Monks Oak, Bradfield St George, Bury St Edmonds IP30 0AY.

F.A.R.M. LTD. (tractors and implements)
   Evesham (0386) 831845.

THE OLD 20 PARTS COMPANY (tractor spares, vintage/modern)
   43 The Wharf, Shardlow, Derby DE7 2HG.

THE PHONE-IN TRADING POST LTD.
   0800 333999.

Sheep Equipment

BATEMAN (Sheepover)
   Cheddleton, Leek, Staffordshire ST13 7EE.

PETER STONE (Sheep Sofa)
   Brookvale, Ringmore, Shalden, Devon.

S. & M. SUPPLIES (Sheep Seat etc.)
   Billingshurst, West Sussex RH14 9JR.

Bibliography

Arakeri, H. R.: *Indian Agriculture* (1982, Oxford & IBH Publishing Co., New Delhi).

Baxter, J.: *The Library of Agricultural and Horticultural Knowledge* (3rd edition, 1834, J. Baxter of Lewes).

Bell, Brian: *Farm Machinery* (3rd edition, 1989, Farming Press).

Boatfield, Graham: *Farm Crops* (2nd edition, 1986, Farming Press).

Bruce, Maye E.: *Common-Sense Compost Making by the Quick Return Method* (revised 1973, reprinted 1977 Faber and Faber).

Burnham, C. P.: *The Soils of England and Wales* (Field Studies Council, London).

Burns, Susan; Lewis, M. R.; Rendell, J.: *Grass Conservation* (1980, University of Reading).

de Bairacli Levy, Juliette: *Herbal Handbook for Farm and Stable* (revised edition 1973, Faber and Faber).

Dench, J. A. L.; Buchanan, W. I.: *Fodder Crops* (1977, University of Reading).

Garner, Lawrence: *Dry Stone Walling* (1984, Shire).

Greaves, Valerie: *Hedgelaying Explained* (National Hedgelaying Society — undated).

Halley, R. J. (ed): *The Agricultural Notebook* (17th edition, 1982, Butterworth Scientific).

Jefferies, Richard: *The Life of the Fields* (orig. 1884, Chatto & Windus; republished 1983, Oxford University Press).

Jefferies, Richard: *The Toilers of the Fields* (orig. 1892, Longmans Green & Co.; republished 1981, Macdonald Futura).

Laity, John: *Profitable Ley Farming* (1948, Crosby Lockwood & Son).

Lockhart, J. A. R.; Wiseman, A. J. L.: *Introduction to Crop Husbandry* (5th edition, 1983, Pergamon Press).

Maycock, S. A.; Hayhurst, John: *The Smallholder's Encyclopaedia* (1950, C. Arthur Pearson Ltd.).

Moore, H. I.: *Grassland Husbandry* (1944, George Allen & Unwin).

Noton, Nicholas H.: *Farm Buildings* (1982, College of Estate Management, Reading).

Robinson, D. H.: *Leguminous Forage Plants* (2nd edition, 1947, Edward Arnold & Co.).

Stowe, E. J.: *Thatching of Rick and Barn* (1954, Landsman's Library Publications, Hartford, Huntingdon).

Thear, David and Katie: *The Home Farm Sourcebook* (2nd edition, 1990, Broad Leys Publishing Co., Saffron Walden).

Watkins, Meike and David: *The Concise Book of Organic Growing and Small Livestock* (self-published 1990, Reigate).

Universities Federation for Animal Welfare (UFAW): *Management and Welfare of Farm Animals* (3rd edition, 1988, Balliere Tindall).

The Compleat Farmer (1975, Mayflower Books Inc., New York — collected articles from *American Agriculturalist* over the past hundred years).

Publications by British Trust for Conservation Volunteers:

Fencing (June 1986).

Hedging (3rd rev, 1988).

Woodlands Management (September 1980)

HMSO/ADAS publications:

Big Bale Silage (Booklet 2408, reprinted 1984).

Energy Conservation in Agriculture (Booklet 2287, 1980).

Farm Buildings (Post-war Building Studies No.17, 1945).

Farm Waste Management (Booklet 2077, reprinted 1985).

Grass as Feed (Booklet 2047; amended 1983).

The Farmer's Weather (Bulletin No.165, 1964).

There are numerous other ADAS publications on all aspects of farming, many of great value to the smallholder. Contact your local office.